SPECIAL **TIME** EDITION

The Science of Emotions

Contents

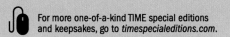 For more one-of-a-kind TIME special editions and keepsakes, go to *timespecialeditions.com*.

Parts of this edition appeared previously in TIME, Health *and* Real Simple.

All About Emotions

FEELINGS ARE THE WORLD'S UNIVERSAL LANGUAGE. BECOMING FLUENT IN THEM CAN HELP YOU UNDERSTAND YOURSELF—AND OTHERS

BY MANDY OAKLANDER

IMAGINE A WORLD WITHOUT EMOTIONS. THE slaphappy highs and shame-riddled lows would even out to a smooth, calm, neutral sensation. It sounds like peaceful Zen bliss, the elusive kind people try to achieve through meditation.

Of course, that's a fantasy. Here on emotionally exhausting Earth, feelings can well up so powerfully that they make you physically sick with fear, or deliriously happy, or head over heels in love.

It may be tempting to sometimes wish your feelings away. But the new science on what emotions are—and what they do for you—reveals that they're vastly underappreciated (especially the bad ones). Without the emotional glue necessary to bind humans together, life would be colorless and isolated.

Emotions, or instinctual states of feeling that stem from our surroundings or mood, have long evaded our understanding (and even that of scientists, who have yet to agree upon an exact definition of the word). Experts long believed that humans have six basic emotions: happiness, sadness, anger, surprise, fear and disgust. But more recent research suggests that there are more than 20, including awe and appall. Mix and match these, and you've got a palette capable of painting the whole human experience.

In many ways, emotions are our universal language. The face's 42 muscles arrange themselves to reflect feelings that humans around the world can recognize, whether instinctively or culturally, without having to be taught.

For the enormous impact they make, emotions are fleeting. They don't last as long as moods, but they are magnitudes more intense. Emotions—so named from the Latin word for "to move"—quite literally set off thoughts and actions. Feeling angry at something in your orbit triggers a cascade of events, not only changing your expression (usually) but also activating your nervous system. Emotions can even change how the body feels, twisting the stomach with anxiety or making the heart race with fear.

When emotions announce themselves so loudly, they're important to listen to. (It's evolutionary: our species wouldn't have been nearly as successful in the face of a lion without fear, the emotion that handily triggers the fight-or-flight response.) In a similar way, simple tweaks to your emotional life can give you an edge, and

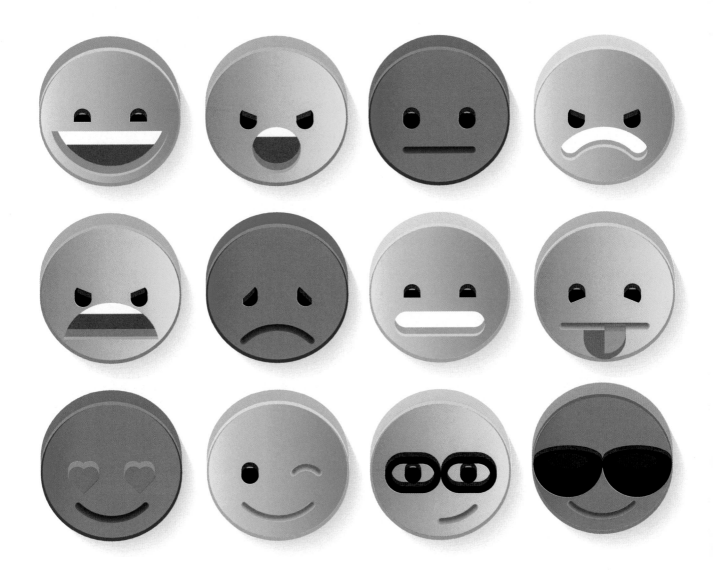

reframing a situation in your mind can actually change how your brain processes the event. Mastering your feelings is the key to fostering a good relationship with yourself and others. With a handle on your emotions, you can even create your own luck.

That doesn't mean you need to force your face into a permanent smile. Negative emotions also serve important functions, researchers are finding; they help us make sense of the complexity of life and can call attention to parts of our lives that need extra care. Studies have shown that suppressing negative emotions often backfires. Luckily, you get good things from gloomy feelings. There's evidence that they encourage careful, more considered thinking, and people in sad

When emotions announce themselves so loudly, they're important to listen to.

moods have been shown to be more generous.

It's important to be able to understand the emotions of people around you, too. Called emotional intelligence, this skill helps you better connect to and comprehend other people—crucial for our highly social species. Reading others well can give you a personal and professional advantage. Emotions also change how we relate to others, and they're contagious. It's not your imagination: being around happy friends really does make things seem brighter.

There's still a lot to learn about our inner emotional lives, but putting to use what scientists have already discovered can make you happier, healthier and more intuitive. That's the best reason yet to get emotional.

PART ONE

Know Yourself

"Knowing others is wisdom;
knowing yourself is
enlightenment."

—LAO TZU,
CHINESE PHILOSOPHER

Unlock Your Emotional Intelligence

UNDERSTANDING WHAT YOU'RE FEELING, AND WHY YOU'RE FEELING IT, CAN GIVE YOU AN EDGE IN LOVE AND LIFE

BY GINNY GRAVES

HOW ARE YOU?

No, really. How are you?

If that sounds like a pointless question, it's because we all typically give the same meaningless answer: "Good!" But what if I wanted the real answer? Could you give one? Can you describe your current emotional state, not with generic words like happy or sad or angry but with more precise language, like apprehensive, discouraged, upbeat, playful or complacent?

It's not easy. I learned this for myself when I tried Mood Meter, an app conceived by researchers at the Yale Center for Emotional Intelligence. Designed to help users identify their current disposition and the reasons for it, the app is one of a number of tools being utilized to enhance emotional intelligence in everyone from schoolchildren to corporate executives. I've always considered myself fairly (OK, highly) introspective. Even so, I found it difficult to discern whether I was merely peeved or truly angered (more later on why the distinction matters) by the fact that my husband, Gordon, forgot to pick up limes for the ceviche I was preparing for guests the next day. This forced me to face a humbling truth: when it comes to pinpointing my emotions, I may be no better than the average fifth-grader.

But self-awareness, painful as it can be, is exactly the point of emotional intelligence. Defined as the ability to identify your own and others' feelings so you can interpret and manage them effectively, the concept of EI was given a framework by researchers Peter Salovey, of Yale, and John Mayer, of the University of New Hampshire, in an article in the scientific journal *Imagination, Cognition and Personality* in 1990. Five years later, Daniel Goleman's book *Emotional Intelligence: Why It Can Matter More Than IQ* introduced the concept to the public—and a worldwide phenomenon was born.

By 2017, hundreds of researchers around the world had parsed the ability—looking at everything from whether people high in EI are less likely to be depressed (yes, probably) to how it contributes to job performance (it helps!)—and the latest studies reveal that it can be beneficial across cultures and in a variety of realms. People higher in EI tend to be agreeable, open to new experiences and conscientious. They're more likely to be mentally and physically healthy, create less interpersonal drama and function more effectively in their careers than those with lower EI. "IQ is critical for landing a job in most professions, but what distinguishes the best team leaders and individual performers is their emotional abilities," says Goleman, now co-chair of the Consortium for Research on Emotional Intelligence in Organizations. What's more, a knack for understanding feelings governs, to a certain degree, everything from the richness of your personal relationships to the level of satisfaction you find in life.

Most studies indicate that you can become more deft at the basic skills of emotional intelligence, even if you don't improve your EI itself (which is partly inherited and partly learned early in life), just as you can get better at math or physics, even though doing so doesn't actually boost your IQ. What do we need to know to utilize—and improve—our

> *You can become more deft at the basic skills of emotional intelligence, just as you can get better at math or physics.*

innate emotional capabilities? And what do we stand to gain by trying?

Tuning in to your feelings

When Socrates enjoined his fellow humans to "know thyself" in the 5th century B.C., he undoubtedly assumed we'd have a better grasp of the subject matter by now, some 2,500 years later. But many of us are still bumbling around in the dark, since we received little overt guidance in our upbringing or education that trained us to be more self-aware and recognize feelings as they happen, the foundational skill of EI. "When you're not conscious of your emotions, you're at their mercy, and they can dictate your behavior for better or worse," says Robin Stern, the associate director of the Yale Center for Emotional Intelligence. But if you know you're feeling irritable, say, or you know what types of stressors make you irritable, whether it's lack of sleep or being stuck in traffic, you're better able to stay in control and defuse a fight with your spouse, for instance, or avoid snapping at your kids. "Self-awareness has meaningful consequences that can impact your relationships and your day-to-day well-being," Stern says.

In one study, researchers at the Yale Center for Emotional Intelligence split teachers into two groups. One wrote about a positive day or experience; the other focused on something negative. Afterward, when both groups graded papers, the teachers who had been primed to feel positive with the writing exercise scored students' work 1 to 2 points higher, on average. As fascinating, when researchers asked participants whether they thought their emotions impacted their decision-making, 85% said no. "I love this study because it shows that not only are your emotions affecting you but they're doing so outside your conscious awareness," says Stern.

Which brings me back to the lime incident that took place while I was trying out the

The Mood Meter app, developed by Yale scientists, guides you through identifying your emotional state, deciding how you want to change it, and choosing strategies to help you achieve your emotional goals.

Mood Meter app (99¢; iPhone or Android). To help you label your feelings, the app has a graph of them. I checked the graph just after Gordon returned from the grocery store. At first I convinced myself that I was just peeved, a low-intensity emotion. Then I realized my neck muscles were tense, and when I shut the fridge door, I did so with gusto. (Some people, like my husband, might say I slammed it.) That's when I knew: my body was in fight-or-flight mode. I wasn't peeved. I was pissed.

Brain studies show that when you're angry, the amygdala, a small structure in the primitive, impulsive limbic center, hijacks your conduct by triggering the release of the stress hormone cortisol, which then surges through your system. Recognizing my true state made me calmer and saved me (barely) from saying something regrettable. Here's why it's so effective: "When you note 'I'm angry,' you shift activity from the limbic system to the prefrontal cortex, the rational part of the brain that helps you think through how best to handle the situation," says Goleman. As neuroscientists like to say, naming an emotion helps you tame it.

Self-awareness takes practice. But mindfulness meditation can make it more natural. The technique—paying attention to your breath, noting nonjudgmentally when your mind is wandering and then gently returning your attention to your breath—trains you to observe what's happening to your emotions rather than get swept away by them. As such, it offers a more sustainable way to understand and stay on top of your moment-by-moment well-being. What's more, a half-hour a day of mindfulness is enough to start inhibiting the amygdala's stress circuitry, possibly by as much as 50%, so you become less emotionally reactive in general, according to Goleman.

Managing your emotions (so they don't manage you)

There are certain unassailable scientific truths. Earth is round. The climate is changing. And if you're going to talk about emotional intelligence, at some point you're going to wind up on the topic of marshmallows. It all goes back to a classic study of 4-year-olds' self-control, conducted at Stanford University in the 1960s. Researchers placed marshmallows on a table in front of a series of 4-year-olds and gave them the following choice: eat one right away, or wait until the researcher returns from running errands and then have two. The kids who were able to resist went on to do better in school and in their careers. This is relevant to emotional intelligence because emotions,

Being able to delay gratification as a child could be a predictor of success in career and life as an adult.

by their nature, create the impulse to act, says Goleman. The second pillar of emotional intelligence is the capacity to resist impulsive behavior—to be a two-marshmallow adult.

Naming your emotions is the first step, because it puts your prefrontal cortex back in the driver's seat. The second step is deciding what to do. Once I realized I was angry, I was able to identify why: I was tired, was short on time and believed that Gordon had disregarded my request. I felt slighted. The Mood Meter suggested that I repeat a calming phrase like "I'm going to take the high road" or get some air, so I took a walk. "Taking a few deep breaths or exercising are effective self-management strategies, because they can give you some time to calm down and think," says Stern.

Different emotions might require other strategies. If you're distracted by worry, it can help to coach yourself through it—"I'm having this thought, but I'm going to get my work done and focus on the problem later," says Stern. If you're ruminating, you might want to reach out to a friend, suggests David Caruso, a management psychologist and co-founder of the Emotional Intelligence Skills Group. "Talking about how you feel and why—and feeling heard and validated—can be incredibly effective at sorting out your thoughts and helping you see your situation more positively," he says.

It's not all about you

Even if you're completely in control of your feelings (which no one is, by the way), you're going to interact with people every day who have varying levels of emotional smarts—and that means you need to be able to perceive others' emotions too. The best way to do that is to see the expressions on their faces, says Mayer, who, along with Salovey, did pioneering work in developing the concept of emotional intelligence. Is it any wonder digital communication creates so many misunderstandings? "When you're texting and emailing, you have nothing to go on but words, and they can be difficult to interpret—although we may be getting better at it since it's such a common way to communicate," he says.

We vary in our ability to decode facial expressions, but paying attention to faces as you interact can help you catch micro-expressions, fleeting facial movements that provide hints to how people really feel. Research shows that you can become more skilled at reading micro-expressions. (Paul Ekman, a professor emeritus in psychology at the University of California, San Francisco, has a short course on his site paulekman.com.) And there's good reason to try, since understanding people's true feelings can have a significant impact on your relationship. In a series of studies that spanned a decade, researchers at the University of Washington found that how often a wife's face showed disgust within a 15-minute conversation, for instance, could predict how likely it was that the couple would separate within four years.

But emotionally intelligent people do more than notice expressions; they tune in to—and share—others' emotions. "Empathy is fundamental to good relationships," says Goleman. You can build that quality, too, research shows, by practicing loving-kindness meditation. Here's how: Hold the thought of someone who is struggling in your mind while silently repeating phrases like "May you be free from suffering. May you have joy and ease." As you meditate, focus on feelings of love. "Compassion meditation enhances empathic concern and activates the same brain circuitry that's triggered when a parent feels love for a child,

> **When you're not aware of your emotions, they can dictate your behavior, for better or worse.**

as well as circuits that register the suffering of others," says Goleman. "You can build your ability to empathize and feel compassion in as little as eight hours of practice, and the longer you practice, the stronger these qualities become."

Having peaceful, happy relationships

The fourth aspect of emotional intelligence is learning how to navigate the sometimes choppy waters of human interaction. This requires awareness of your own emotions and someone else's—and behaving in a way that takes both into account. "There are responsive strategies that you can deploy in the moment as well as preventive strategies," says Caruso. If you're chatting with a friend or neighbor and the conversation suddenly becomes heated, you might try changing the topic to something neutral so you don't end up in an argument—that's a responsive strategy. Or, if you know that a certain subject tends to trigger conflict, you might prevent the problem by avoiding that sensitive topic altogether.

One of the most powerful tools for effectively managing interpersonal challenges, Caruso adds, is reappraisal, or putting a more positive spin on someone else's bad behavior. For instance, instead of viewing my husband's forgetfulness as evidence that he doesn't prioritize my needs, I could see it as a sign that he's stressed, overwhelmed and tired too. "Remind yourself of a time when you've made a similar mistake. That helps you be more compassionate," Caruso says. That was all it took. In the time-honored tradition of marriage, I cut my husband some slack.

In other words, it helps to have humility—and to understand and acknowledge your own shortcomings. In fact, that may be one of the surest signs of high emotional intelligence, says Mayer: "People who are extremely confident of their emotional abilities are the most likely to be profoundly wrong."

Happiness Is...

IF NOT A WARM PUPPY, THEN WHAT?
THREE WRITERS EXPLORE THIS EVER-CHANGING
AND AT TIMES ELUSIVE EMOTION

The History of Happiness

BY MARCIA MENTER

WE AMERICANS BELIEVE THAT WE HAVE THE right to be happy. In America today, we seem to equate the pursuit of happiness with the pursuit of success. Popular self-help books suggest that if we practice positive thinking, we will magically create great relationships, jobs we love and more money than we know how to spend. This sounds like an awful lot to demand of ourselves—and furthermore, it's not my idea of happiness.

It's also not what Thomas Jefferson had in mind when he drafted the Declaration. He saw the pursuit of happiness through the lens of certain ancient Greek philosophers: as something basic to human nature, essential for living a good and virtuous life. He may have borrowed the phrase from the Enlightenment philosopher John Locke, who wrote that in order to seek "true and solid happiness," we need to learn to distinguish real happiness from the imaginary kind. Before we gallop off after something we want, in other words, we need to think long and hard about whether it will actually make us happy. Getting everything you want in life will not necessarily do that—as you already know if you came of age during the second wave of the feminist movement, when women were supposed to try to "have it all." But slogging through the messy struggle of a life can yield moments of pure happiness, and those moments, I believe, add immeasurably to the world.

I remember, nearly 20 years ago, standing in front of the Basilique du Sacré-Coeur, high above Paris. It was one of those raw, rainy mornings that drive the cold right into your bones. I'm not a Catholic or even a Christian. Nevertheless, I had a Moment. As I started down the 300 steps to the street, I suddenly felt that everything about me—my ineptly dyed auburn hair, my fraying wool-twill coat, my cold feet in their ugly shoes—was perfect. My unsuitable career was perfect. My furtive, irrational loves were perfect. I was exactly who I needed to be, and this filled me with a quiet,

Dante Alighieri with *Divine Comedy* in his hand, entrance to hell on the left, heaven above and purgatory in background; detail from fresco, Florence, Italy, 1465

complete happiness that had nothing to do with what I had or had not achieved in life. The moment passed as quietly as it came, but I kept it—stuck it under my good old twill coat—as a sign that whatever track I was on was the right one. That, in fact, almost any track, followed in the right spirit, could be the right one. Happiness comes in small moments while you're pursuing the big stuff. After a while, the small moments become the point. This is especially true in tough times. When the world seems to be falling apart, you still have your little touchstones of joy.

At age 20, I encountered a line in Dante's

I've dug for myself, there are other roadblocks I haven't gotten around—and may never get around. Furthermore, I'm mortal, so I don't have forever to perfect my life. But I can still make pleasure my guide. Dante taught me that even a short life is a very long journey, and we all need provisions for the trip. We need good food, good stories and people to share them with. We need a sense of proportion and a sense of the absurd. We need to have as good a time as we can, because, otherwise, what's the point?

The Science of Happiness

BY LESLIE PEPPER

MEASURING HAPPINESS IS A TRICKY BUSINESS. Still, that hasn't stopped individuals and institutions from trying to gauge how happy people are in an attempt to determine what it is exactly that brings joy. Former British prime minister David Cameron even proposed polling residents of the United Kingdom annually about their well-being.

There's a benefit to making sure people are happy: happiness is a cornerstone of productivity. Countless studies have shown that those with a skip in their step typically have better jobs, are evaluated more positively by their bosses and make more money. They are also more charitable and more satisfied with their marriages, and they have stronger immune systems.

These findings raise a couple of questions, though. First off: Does happiness cause all those terrific things to happen, or is it the other way around? Sonja Lyubomirsky, a professor of psychology at the University of California, Riverside, and the author of *The How of Happiness*, wondered this too. So in 2005, she and her research team reviewed approximately 250 studies conducted over the previous 25 years and determined that, lo and behold, being happy brings you great things. The second question: Exactly how high on life do you need to be to reap these rewards? (Do you have to be a 9 on a scale of 1 to 10, or is being a 7 sufficient?) In this case, no one really knows. Happiness is extremely subjective, says Tal Ben-Shahar, a

Divine Comedy that I've never forgotten. Dante has been guided by his idol, the Roman poet Virgil, through Hell and Purgatory and is about to enter the Earthly Paradise. Virgil leaves him at this point, saying, "Take henceforth your pleasure as your guide." In Hell, Dante has seen human beings make every kind of misery for themselves without knowing how to escape. In Purgatory, he has watched people atone for their destructive behaviors. Over the course of his journey, he has acquired the wisdom to know where true happiness lies, and now his heart will unerringly guide him there.

I don't know about you, but I'm not there yet. Then again, I'm not expecting perfect happiness. Like most of us, I'm happy in some ways, less happy in others. Although I've managed to clamber out of some pretty deep holes

Do something that serves a larger purpose, whether it's a job you find meaningful or volunteer work in the community. "Doing good can make you feel good," says psychology professor Barry Schwartz.

professor of psychology at the Interdisciplinary Center in Herzliya, Israel, and the author of *Being Happy*. What constitutes radiant joy for one person might not even rate as a good mood for another.

What the experts do know is that you can increase your sense of happiness, no matter where you happen to fall on the emotional spectrum. And that's a fairly new discovery. Scientists used to believe that people had a genetically predetermined happiness "set point" and could do little to alter it.

But research has largely disproved that idea. A study published in 2010 in *Proceedings of the National Academy of Sciences* looked at data gathered from surveys of 60,000 adults con-

ducted over the course of 25 years and found that other factors play key roles as well. "Life goals and choices have as much or more impact on life satisfaction than variables routinely described as important in previous research," wrote Bruce Headey, of the Melbourne Institute of Applied Economic and Social Research in Australia. Lyubomirsky takes it one step further: Of the approximately 50% of our happiness that isn't biologically driven, she says, 10% is connected to life circumstances (you're beautiful, say, or uniquely talented). But that leaves 40% unaccounted for—and up to us to shape.

Unfortunately, that doesn't guarantee much in terms of jump-starting joy. As Daniel Gilbert, a professor of psychology at Harvard University and the author of *Stumbling on Happiness*, notes, most of us don't always know what makes us happy. This is largely due to a phenomenon called hedonic adaptation: after an initial rush, we quickly adapt to whatever it is we think will make us happier and soon begin to take it for granted, at which point it no longer brings contentment. "For example, when you step into an air-conditioned room on a hot and humid day, you feel spectacular," says Barry Schwartz, a professor of psychology at Swarthmore College and a co-author of *Practical Wisdom*. "But after about five minutes, it's simply what it is: comfortable, but no longer pleasurable." The same principle holds true for money. We think the more we have, the happier we'll be. But this is not the case. David Myers, a professor of psychology at Hope College, found that there is little correlation between cash and contentment. The same holds for a dream date or a coveted job. One study followed high-level managers for five years and found that although voluntarily changing jobs brought a quick increase in satisfaction, that emotional high dissipated within the year.

The secret to manipulating the 40% of happiness that is within your control lies in other, nonmaterial areas. There are several frequently cited and easy ways to tip the happiness scales in your favor. One, repeat behaviors that have made you happy in the past, such as going on a ski trip with friends or taking the scenic route home from the grocery store. Two, immerse yourself in whatever you're doing. (This is a state psychologists refer to as "flow"—you get caught up in something that feels bigger than yourself while staying present in the moment.) And three, do something that serves a larger purpose, whether it's a job you find meaningful or volunteer work in the community. "Doing good can make you feel good," says Schwartz.

Gretchen Rubin is living proof that you can boost your happiness levels. One rainy afternoon a few years ago, she realized that although she had a good life and was fairly happy, she knew she could appreciate life more. So she decided to dedicate the next year to making small adjustments to feel more at peace—and to write about it in what became a best seller, *The Happiness Project*. She cleared her cluttered closets. She tackled nagging tasks, like going to a dermatologist for a skin check. She vowed to focus on friends. She willed herself to meet three new people in every new situation, and she used a computer program to remember friends' birthdays. By the year's end, she truly felt happier.

Rubin couldn't alter her genetic predisposition for happiness; none of us can. But she did ratchet up her levels of happiness by changing her everyday behaviors. And though these tweaks may seem inconsequential at the time you're doing them, they can make a lasting and meaningful impact on your well-being. If that's not reason enough to smile, what is?

The Psychology of Happiness

BY MEG WOLITZER

"LET'S ALL GO AROUND THE CIRCLE AND TAKE turns telling everyone what makes us happy," our third-grade teacher said as she stood before the class, looking svelte and resplendent in the kind of paisley minidress that was big at the time. Even from my presexual, nerd-girl vantage point, I understood that she herself was happy and that this, of course, was why she had chosen the exercise. The class across the hall, led by a gloomy teacher in a burnt-orange crocheted shawl, would never have been instructed to go around the circle and proclaim the particulars of their joy. They might, instead, have been coaxed into a heated discussion of Incan farming, but that was about it. Our teacher was happy, truly happy, and like most happy people, she wanted everyone to know it.

One by one, the kids in our class said that snow days made them happy; getting presents made them happy; doing nice things for other people made them (supposedly) happy; Carvel made them happy. When it was my turn, I believe I volunteered that my dachshund made me happy. Finally, when it was our teacher's turn, she pronounced that we, her students, made her happy, though of course we knew better.

Her happiness, we were certain, had nothing to do with us. She was in love—and someone loved her back. This was the source of her not-so-secret hidden happiness, and it served as an engine that roared her through every single school day.

Happiness, it seems to me here in the middle of my life, long after my dachshund has gone, and long after snow days have ceased to have much relevance, and even after most presents have stopped mattering to me, is a slippery thing. The nature of it changes as quickly as our own lives do.

For years—a period that stretched from high school through college and then deep into the murk of my 20s—my friends and I were intensely aware of all our feeling-states and desires, whether good or bad. Several of us went to the same therapist, whose name was Martha, and her office had a cocktail-party-with-a-turnstile quality to it. "Oh, hey, how are you, Meg?" someone might say on her way out. "Great shoes." Personal happiness was something we deliberately strove for, often in the form of men, women, a first big professional success or a cheap walk-up apartment, though of course we were often beset by dramatic sorrow (cue Martha). This period of flux went on for a long time. Life was peppered with love and excitement and tears, and my friends and I had learned to be human barometers for our own happiness.

But then time sped forward, and although the actual catalysts for happiness continued to change, a strange thing happened: happiness seemed less relevant as a goal, and things seemed less awful when it didn't appear. And now the truth is that at this particular moment in my life, I no longer think in terms of "happy" and "unhappy," the way I did when I was in third grade, or as a young woman in my own era's version of a paisley minidress. It's not only that I've aged but that the world has too.

Everyone talks incessantly about stress now, and how it has changed our lives and made us so unhappy. Less obviously, I think stress has also changed the quest for happiness itself, making it more aggressive and occupying more of our time. Ever since antide-pressants and sexual-enhancement drugs hit the airwaves and ever since we were told that we had a right to our happiness, damn it, and that we could ask for it—no, demand it—from our doctors, spouses, friends or employers, it seems that the desire for happiness has increasingly become a source of anxiety.

Which is why I have taken a few steps back. At this point, being happy is about having the space to appreciate the ordinary things that do in fact make me "happy," though at first glance they might not be seen that way. An absence of chaos; an absence of phone calls with disturbing news; an absence of business emails that upend your day and demand attention right then and there; no acutely ill parents; no fragile children calling shakily from college. Being able to sit down with a glass of wine and some really good, tiny little olives with your husband; having a nice meal with your kids that's not rushed or fraught. These seem like small things, perhaps pedestrian things, but I protect them fiercely, knowing that on the other side of an imaginary wall waits the possibility that all of them will soon be gone and that something terrible will replace them.

But I no longer quake in fear. I used to think that happiness was something a person was so lucky to find that, like Lord Voldemort (a.k.a. He Who Must Not Be Named), it should never actually be mentioned. Now, with happiness taking on a new, modest cast, the fear of losing it is smaller too.

You might think: Good god, woman! This isn't happiness. Happiness has wild colors and flavors; it involves bodies draped across a bed, or things that come in gift wrap. Or even, once in a while, Carvel. Don't you want any of that?

Of course I do. But being allowed to enjoy some of the more modest pieces of my life happens right now to be my own personal Carvel; my own dachshund, gift-wrapped present, snow day and secret lover. Perhaps for most of us—or anyway, for me—happiness has gotten smaller over time, becoming endlessly and exquisitely refined, though somehow never diminished.

> *Happiness is a slippery thing. The nature of it changes as quickly as our own lives do.*

8 EASY WAYS TO BE HAPPIER

NEED A LIFT? THESE LITTLE, SCIENCE-BACKED MOVES
JUST MAY PUT YOU IN A SUNNIER FRAME OF MIND

BY SARA REISTAD-LONG

1. REMEMBER WHENCE YOU CAME

Don't underestimate the power of nostalgia. When you swap stories about the Bad Prom of 1989 or the Amazing Cross-Country Trip of 1971 with others, you view yourself in a more positive light and form tighter bonds, says Dan Buettner, the author of *Thrive: Finding Happiness the Blue Zones Way*, a book about the happiest regions in the world. He also recommends "land-mining your home with photos and memorabilia, so you're constantly reminded of your history." Adorning a hallway or a highly trafficked room with sentimental objects is a good way to start. (See, Grandma knew what she was doing.)

2. DON'T DWELL

Mulling over past failures can be tempting (you feel as if you're gaining insights and finding answers). But over time this behavior may lead to feelings of helplessness. Studies show that ruminators are more likely to be depressed, due to a downward spiral of emotions. First you begin obsessing, which makes you lack the mental clarity to come up with potentially good solutions to problems; as a result, you lose confidence and feel unhappy, research has found. So instead of going over something again and again, distract yourself with a movie or a game. (How about Scattergories?)

3. SPREAD THE WEALTH

Giving away money can make you happier than spending it on yourself, studies show. The

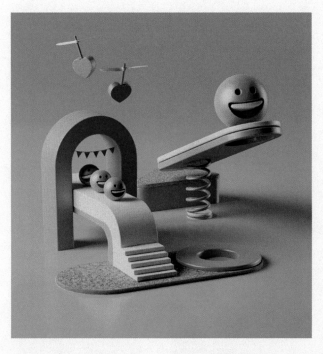

same may be true of buying things for others rather than yourself. So if you're going for coffee, take a colleague's order and foot the bill. Pick up a treat for a friend that you would normally impulse-buy for yourself at the checkout counter. And tip generously. The payoff will be yours.

4. EAT A SNACK AROUND 2 P.M.

That's when levels of serotonin, a brain chemical that helps regulate mood, can take a nosedive, according to Eric Braverman, a physician in New York and the author of *The Edge Effect*. Ideally, choose one that contains mood-boosting nutritional powerhouses, like B vitamins (B6, B12 and folic acid, found in many natural and fortified foods) and complex carbohydrates (try whole grains).

5. GET A MOVE ON

"For some people, exercising at high intensity three times a week for just 30 minutes at a time can provide the same benefits as some of the most powerful psychiatric medications," says psychologist Tal Ben-Shahar. Research suggests that during that half-hour of exercise, the human body can increase the production of a protein called brain-derived neurotrophic factor, which can have an antidepressant effect. Yoga, for its part, seems to have additional calming (and happy-making) effects on both the brain and the parasympathetic nervous system.

6. LIMIT YOUR OPTIONS

"When you make a choice, you generally want the best," says psychologist Barry Schwartz. "That means you

tend to consider everything that's available, which can be overwhelming." Not to mention stressful and anxiety-producing. When you find yourself paralyzed by indecision, whether you're shopping for a new car or a new nail-polish color, quickly try to whittle your options to a few choices. Then pick one and move on.

7. START BAKING

Or learn to hula. Or join a quilting bee. Just find something that occupies 100% of your attention while you're engaged in it. You'll be more motivated and focused—feelings that promote happiness, says Mihaly Csikszentmihalyi, a professor of psychology and management at Claremont Graduate University. Case in point: Buettner says that in Denmark (characterized as the most thriving country in the world when it comes to well-being, according to a World Gallup Poll), a majority of the population reports belonging to a social club.

8. MAKE YOUR BED

"When I was researching my book on happiness, this was the number one most impactful change that people brought up over and over," says author Gretchen Rubin. It turns out people are happier when everyday tasks in their lives are completed. And if hospital corners don't do it for you, test out other small ways to make your life more efficient and pleasant. Shoot for concrete changes: hanging a key hook in your entryway, finally moving your banking online. Or they can be behavioral—say, cracking the code to curing your persistent tardiness.

The Upside of Bad Moods

NO ONE LIKES TO BE CRANKY, BUT IT TURNS OUT THAT "NEGATIVE" FEELINGS HAVE SURPRISING PERKS. IN THIS EXCERPT FROM THE BOOK *EMOTIONAL AGILITY*, A HARVARD MEDICAL SCHOOL PSYCHOLOGIST EXPLAINS WHY MAKING PEACE WITH OUR ANGER, FEAR AND SADNESS CAN USHER IN A MORE AUTHENTIC SORT OF JOY

BY SUSAN DAVID

IT'S BEEN MORE THAN 50 YEARS SINCE THE SMILEY FACE—THAT bright yellow circle with the schematic grin and black-dot eyes—first appeared. Hundreds of millions of HAVE A NICE DAY buttons, T-shirts and coffee mugs later, it's as iconic as the red, white and blue. (And why not? After all, the "pursuit of happiness" is front and center in America's Declaration of Independence.)

In the digital age, the smiley face morphed into the emoticons and emojis that pop up everywhere. And with each advance—or, some might say, regression—in our consumer culture, in which marketers hustle to fulfill desires we didn't even know we had, the blissed-out state of Mr. Smiley becomes ever more the holy grail, the organizing principle of our existence.

Wait a minute. Isn't happiness why we're here? Isn't happiness good for us?

Given a choice, we'd probably prefer to be happy all the time, and there are advantages to that pleasurable state. More "positive" emotion is linked to a lower risk of various psychological illnesses, including depression, anxiety and borderline personality disorder.

Positive emotions also drive us to success, help us make better decisions, reduce the risk of disease and allow us to live longer.

In some cases, they even help broaden how we think and act by directing our attention to new information and opportunities. They help build vital social, physical and cognitive resources that lead to positive outcomes and affiliations.

Considering all of this, you might presume that happiness ranks right up there with food and sunshine in its contribution to human well-being. But it is possible to have too much of a good thing—to not only be too happy but also experience the wrong types of happiness, and to go about trying to find happiness in the wrong ways and at the wrong time.

I'm not saying it's better to go around in a funk all the time. But I hope to get you to keep the pursuit of happiness in perspective and to see your "negative" emotions in a new and more accepting light. In fact, I strongly submit that describing them as "negative" only perpetuates the myth that these useful feelings are, you know, negative.

The trouble with happiness

When we are overly cheerful, we tend to neglect important threats and dangers. It's not too big a stretch to suggest that being excessively happy could kill you. You might engage in riskier behaviors like drinking too much ("A fifth round on me!"), binge eating ("Mmm, more cake!"), skipping birth control ("What could possibly go wrong?") and using drugs ("Let's party!"). An excess of freewheeling giddiness and a relative absence of more sober emotions can even be a marker for mania, a dangerous symptom of psychological illness.

People with high happiness levels sometimes exhibit behavior that is actually more rigid. That's because mood affects the way our brains process information. When life is good, and when the environment is safe and familiar, we tend not to think long and hard about anything too challenging—which helps explain why highly positive people can be less creative than those with a more moderate level of positive emotion.

> ## When we are overly cheerful, we tend to neglect important threats and dangers.

When we're in an "everything is awesome!" mood, we're far more likely to jump to conclusions and resort to stereotypes. The happy more often place disproportionate emphasis on early information and disregard or minimize later details. This typically takes the form of the halo effect, in which, for example, we automatically assume that the cute guy we've just met at the party is kind, just because he wears cool clothes and tells funny jokes. Or we decide that the bespectacled, middle-aged man with a briefcase is more intelligent or reliable, say, than the 22-year-old blonde wearing hot-pink shorts.

Our so-called negative emotions encourage slower, more systematic cognitive processing. We rely less on quick conclusions and pay more attention to subtle details that matter. (OK, the guy is hot, and he seems into you, but why is he hiding his wedding-ring hand behind his back?) Isn't it interesting that the most famous fictional detectives are notably grumpy? And that the most carefree kid in high school is rarely valedictorian?

"Negative" moods summon a more attentive, accommodating thinking style that leads you to really examine facts in a fresh and creative way. It's when we're in a bit of a funk that we focus and dig down. People in negative moods tend to be less gullible and more skeptical, while happy folks may accept easy answers and trust false smiles. Who wants to question surface truth when everything is going so well? So the happy person goes ahead and signs on the dotted line.

The paradox of happiness is that deliberately striving for it is fundamentally incompatible with the nature of happiness itself. Real happiness comes through activities you engage in for their own sake rather than for some extrinsic reason, even when the reason is something as seemingly benevolent as the desire to be happy.

Striving for happiness establishes an expectation and confirms the saying that expectations are resentments waiting to happen.

Forcing yourself to act chipper isn't healthy, but neither is brooding. (Both involve burying difficult emotions.)

That's why holidays and family events are often disappointing, if not downright depressing. Our expectations are so high that it's almost inevitable we'll be let down.

In one study, participants were given a fake newspaper article that praised the advantages of happiness, while a control group read an article that made no mention of happiness. Both groups then watched randomly assigned film clips that were either happy or sad. The participants who had been induced to value happiness by reading the article came away from viewing the "happy film" feeling less happy than those in the control group who had watched the same film. Placing too high a value on happiness increased their expectations for how things "should be" and thus set them up for disappointment.

In another study, participants were asked to listen to Stravinsky's "The Rite of Spring," a piece of music so discordant and jarring that it caused a riot at its 1913 debut. Some participants were told to "try to make yourself feel as happy as possible" while they listened to the music. Afterward, they evaluated themselves as being less happy compared with a control group that was not chasing Mr. Smiley.

The aggressive pursuit of happiness is also isolating. In yet another study, the higher the participants ranked happiness on their lists of objectives or goals, the more they described themselves as lonely on daily self-evaluations.

Happiness also comes in a variety of cultural variations that open up the possibility of being happy in the wrong way. In North America, happiness tends to be defined in terms of personal accomplishment (including pleasure), whereas in East Asia, happiness is associated with social harmony. Chinese Americans prefer contentment, while Americans with European backgrounds prefer excitement. Japanese culture is built around loyalty, with its connection to guilt, whereas American culture embodies more socially disengaged emotions, such as pride or anger. To be happy within a given culture depends more than a little on how in sync your feelings are with that culture's definition of happiness.

In short, chasing after happiness can be just as self-defeating as brooding and bottling up your emotions. It's yet another coping mechanism for discomfort with "negative" emotions and our unwillingness to endure anything even remotely associated with the dark side.

Negative emotions can help you assess a situation and get your point across in a nonconfrontational way.

Good news for grumps

While it's certainly not healthy to constantly stew in negative emotions, there are some positive things that sadness, anger, guilt and fear can do:

Help you form arguments

You're more likely to use concrete information, be more attuned to the situation at hand and be less prone to making judgment errors, all of which lends an aura of expertise and authority that can make you a more persuasive writer and speaker.

Improve your memory

One study found that shoppers remembered much more information about the interior of a store on cold, gloomy days when they weren't feeling so exuberant than they did on sunny days when life felt like a breeze. Research also shows that when we're in a not-so-good mood, we're less likely to inadvertently corrupt our memories by incorporating misleading information.

Encourage perseverance

When you already feel great, why push yourself? On academic tests, an individual in a more somber mood will try to answer more questions—and get more of them right—than he or she will when feeling cheerful.

Help you know when to walk away

People in negative moods pay more attention to fairness and are more apt to reject unfair offers.

Boost your ability to reason

In a study of people with strong political opinions, those who were angry chose to read more articles that opposed their positions instead of practicing confirmation bias, the common tendency to seek out info that supports what we already believe to be true. After exploring these contrary views, they were more willing to change their minds. It seems that anger produces a "nail the opposition" mentality that encourages us to explore what the other guy has to say in order to tear it apart—ironically leaving the door open to being persuaded.

Extracted from *Emotional Agility*, by Susan David © 2016, published by Avery, an imprint of Penguin Publishing Group, a division of Penguin Random House, LLC.

FEAR FACTOR

WHAT WE GET OUT OF HAUNTED HOUSES, HORROR FLICKS AND THINGS THAT GO BUMP IN THE NIGHT, ACCORDING TO MARGEE KERR, A SOCIOLOGIST AND THE AUTHOR OF *SCREAM: CHILLING ADVENTURES IN THE SCIENCE OF FEAR*

BY YOLANDA WIKIEL

What's the theory on why we like scary things?
Scaring ourselves is a way of hijacking our threat response and experiencing heightened emotion. Think of a child popping out from behind a door to frighten her mom. Tapping into the startle response is an easy way to feel a thrill. Whenever we mess with our body's equilibrium (like on a roller coaster), it brings that same sort of excitement.

But it's not fun for everyone, right?
No. Research has found that there are big influences in childhood development and exposure that may affect some people's experience of stress and joy. If, for example, your first experience watching a horror flick was traumatic, you may not enjoy it later on in life. But the studies also found that there are genetic differences. People with certain dopamine genetic expressions tend to be more thrill-seeking.

Is there a difference between fear of real danger and the fear we experience in, say, a theme-park haunted house?
The physical reaction is the same: Endorphins release to block pain signals, and noradrenaline flows to kick up the metabolism so that we can turn any available sugar into energy. The heart rate increases. It's what's going on in our heads that's different. As soon as we recognize that we're safe

or in a controlled space, we can interpret the fear as enjoyable rather than threatening.

You've done work with several haunted attractions.
I consult with the designers on how to apply the science of fear. For instance, I'll suggest putting an auditory scare after a bright light to mix up the types of startles so that they tap different senses. And I have a research lab at some of the attractions, where I set up willing participants with monitoring devices to measure brain activity and heart rate. They take surveys to report their moods before and after.

What have you discovered?
Our data shows that, for people who choose to do scary types of activities, anxiety and stress go down and mood goes up afterward.

Why is that?
The theory is that when we go into threat-response mode, we don't have as much rational or ruminating thought, because our bodies are very much grounded in physical experience.

And thinking less can be relaxing.
Yes, and these folks seem to use thrills and chills to get to that point of a blank mind.

Does that mind-set last?
What we're studying now is the potential that these scary experiences reset the bar on stress tolerance. You may go through a haunted house and come out thinking that the things you were worrying about before—say, confronting your boss—aren't as scary.

So should we push ourselves to watch a horror flick?
Not unless you want to. The choice is key. If you know that you don't like to be scared, you probably won't get the positive benefits from it.

What about kids—do they benefit too?
It depends on the kid. I cringe when I see parents pushing a child through a haunted house. If the child doesn't yet have the cognitive ability to take on other people's perspectives, he can't understand that a fake-scary place is fake. I wouldn't recommend taking a kid under 7 to a haunted house or a scary movie.

What are you afraid of?
I used to have nightmares of driving off a bridge, and recently when there was construction on a bridge where I was driving, it brought back all those fears.

Do you have any parting advice?
Never tell a child that she shouldn't be scared of something that seems scary. Fear is natural, and it's critical to be able to trust your threat response.

Why Do We Cry?

SCIENCE IS CLOSE TO SOLVING THE MYSTERY OF TEARS (AND WHY SOME PEOPLE DON'T SHED THEM AT ALL)

BY MANDY OAKLANDER

MICHAEL TRIMBLE, A BEHAVIORAL NEUROLOGIST WITH THE UN-usual distinction of being one of the world's leading experts on crying, was about to be interviewed on a BBC radio show when an assistant asked him a strange question: How come some people don't cry at all?

The staffer went on to explain that a colleague of hers insisted he never cries. She'd even taken him to see *Les Misérables*, certain it would jerk a tear or two, but his eyes stayed dry. Trimble was stumped. He and the handful of other scientists who study human crying tend to focus their research on wet eyes, not dry ones, so before the broadcast began, he set up an email address—nocrying10@gmail.com—and on the air asked listeners who never cry to contact him. Within hours, Trimble had received hundreds of messages.

"We don't know anything about people who don't cry," says Trimble, now professor emeritus at University College London. In fact, there's also a lot scientists don't know—or can't agree on—about people who do cry. Charles Darwin once declared emotional tears "purposeless," and nearly 150 years later, emotional crying remains one of the human body's more confounding mysteries. Though some other species shed tears reflexively as a result of pain or irritation, humans are the only creatures whose waterworks can be triggered by their feelings. In babies, tears have the obvious and crucial role of soliciting attention and care from adults. But what about in grown-ups? That's less clear. It's obvious that strong emotions trigger them, but why?

There's a surprising dearth of hard facts about so fundamental a part of the human experience. Scientific doubt that crying has any real benefit beyond the physiological—tears lubricate the eyes—has persisted for centuries. Beyond that, researchers have generally focused their attention more on emotions than on physiological processes that can appear to be their byproducts. "Scientists are not interested in the butterflies in our stomach, but in love," writes Ad Vingerhoets, a professor at Tilburg University in the Netherlands and the world's foremost expert on crying, in his 2013 book *Why Only Humans Weep*.

But crying is more than a symptom of sadness, as Vingerhoets and others are showing. It's triggered by a range of feelings—from empathy and surprise to anger and grief—and unlike those butterflies that flap around invisibly when we're in love, tears are a signal that others can see. That insight is central to the newest thinking about the science of crying.

Tears throughout time

Darwin wasn't the only one with strong opinions about why humans cry. By some calculations, people have been speculating about where tears come from and why humans shed them since about 1500 B.C. For centuries, people thought tears originated in the heart; the Old Testament describes tears as the byproduct of when the heart's material weakens and turns into water, says Vingerhoets. In Hippocrates's time, around 400 B.C., it was thought that the mind was the trigger for tears. A prevailing theory in the 1600s held that emotions—especially love—heated the heart, which generated water vapor in order to

cool itself down. The heart vapor would then rise to the head, condense near the eyes and escape as tears.

Finally, in 1662, a Danish scientist named Niels Stensen discovered that the lacrimal gland was the proper origin point of tears. That's when scientists began to unpack what possible benefit could be conferred by fluid that springs from the eye. Stensen's theory: tears were simply a way to keep the eye moist.

Few scientists have devoted their studies to figuring out why humans weep, but those who do don't agree. In his book, Vingerhoets lists eight competing theories. Some are flat-out ridiculous, like the 1960s view that humans evolved from aquatic apes and tears helped us live in saltwater. Other theories persist despite lack of proof, like the idea popularized by biochemist William Frey in the early 1980s that crying removes toxic substances from the blood that build up during times of stress.

> *Humans are the only creatures whose waterworks can be triggered by their feelings.*

Evidence is mounting in support of some new, more plausible theories. One is that tears trigger social bonding and human connection. We cry from a very early age in order to bring about a connection with others. Humans are born into the world vulnerable and physically unequipped to deal with anything on our own. Even though we get physically and emotionally more capable as we mature, grown-ups never quite age out of the occasional bout of helplessness. "Crying signals to yourself and other people that there's some important problem that is at least temporarily beyond your ability to cope," says Jonathan Rottenberg, an emotion researcher and professor of psychology at the University of South Florida. "It very much is an outgrowth of where crying comes from originally."

New research is also showing that tears appear to elicit a response in other people that mere distress does not. In a study published in 2016 in the journal *Motivation and Emotion*, Vingerhoets and his colleagues found that tears activate compassion. When test subjects

Teary Tics

For hundreds of years, scientists have been trying to understand the evolutionary and biological purpose of human tears. These illustrations, based on the work of grief researcher and psychologist Hans Znoj, depict the 12 facial contortions commonly made by people when they cry.

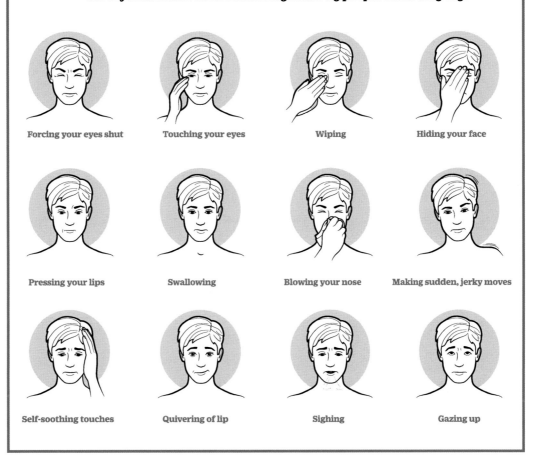

Forcing your eyes shut Touching your eyes Wiping Hiding your face

Pressing your lips Swallowing Blowing your nose Making sudden, jerky moves

Self-soothing touches Quivering of lip Sighing Gazing up

were shown a photograph of someone crying, compared with the same photo with the tears digitally removed, they were much more likely to want to reach out and reported feeling more connected to that person.

Scientists have also found some evidence that emotional tears are chemically different from the ones people shed while chopping onions—which may help explain why crying sends such a strong emotional signal to others. In addition to the enzymes, lipids, metabolites and electrolytes that make up any tears, emotional tears contain more protein. One hypothesis is that this higher protein content

makes emotional tears more viscous, so they stick to the skin more strongly and run down the face more slowly, making them more likely to be seen by others.

Tears also show others that we're vulnerable, and vulnerability is critical to human connection. "The same neuronal areas of the brain are activated by seeing someone emotionally aroused as being emotionally aroused oneself," says Trimble. "There must have been some point in time, evolutionarily, when the tear became something that automatically set off empathy and compassion in another. Actually being able to cry emotionally, and being

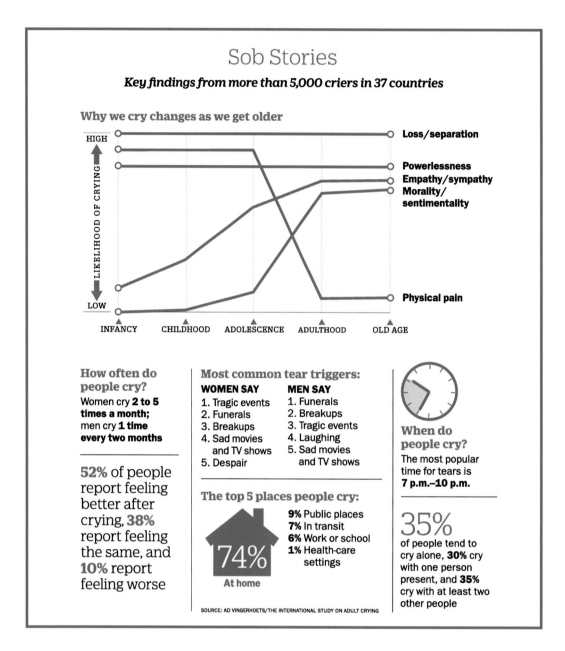

Sob Stories

Key findings from more than 5,000 criers in 37 countries

Why we cry changes as we get older

LIKELIHOOD OF CRYING — HIGH ... LOW

INFANCY   CHILDHOOD   ADOLESCENCE   ADULTHOOD   OLD AGE

Loss/separation
Powerlessness
Empathy/sympathy
Morality/sentimentality
Physical pain

How often do people cry?
Women cry **2 to 5 times a month;** men cry **1 time every two months**

52% of people report feeling better after crying, **38%** report feeling the same, and **10%** report feeling worse

Most common tear triggers:

WOMEN SAY
1. Tragic events
2. Funerals
3. Breakups
4. Sad movies and TV shows
5. Despair

MEN SAY
1. Funerals
2. Breakups
3. Tragic events
4. Laughing
5. Sad movies and TV shows

The top 5 places people cry:

74% At home

9% Public places
7% In transit
6% Work or school
1% Health-care settings

When do people cry?
The most popular time for tears is **7 p.m.–10 p.m.**

35% of people tend to cry alone, **30%** cry with one person present, and **35%** cry with at least two other people

SOURCE: AD VINGERHOETS/THE INTERNATIONAL STUDY ON ADULT CRYING

---

able to respond to that, is a very important part of being human."

A less heartwarming theory focuses on crying's ability to manipulate others. Researchers believe that just as babies use tears as a tool for getting what they need, so do adults—whether they're aware of it or not. "We learn early on that crying has this really powerful effect on other people," Rottenberg says. "It can neutralize anger very powerfully," which is part of the reason he thinks tears are so integral to fights between lovers, particularly when someone feels guilty and wants the other person's forgiveness. "Adults like to think they're

beyond that, but I think a lot of the same functions carry forth," he says.

A small 2011 study in the journal *Science* that was widely cited—and widely hyped by the media—suggested that tears from women contained a substance that inhibited the sexual arousal of men. When 24 men sniffed real tears, they felt less aroused by photos of women's faces, and when 50 men sniffed them, they had sharply reduced testosterone levels in their saliva than they did when they sniffed the control saline. "I won't pretend to be surprised that it generated all the wrong headlines," says Noam Sobel, one of the study's authors and a professor of neurobiology at the Weizmann Institute of Science in Israel. Tears might be lowering sexual arousal—but the bigger story, he thinks, is that they might be reducing aggression, which the study didn't look at. Men's tears may well have the same effect. He and his group are currently wading through the 160-plus molecules in tears to see if there's one responsible.

The dry-eyed loner

What all of this means for people who don't cry is a question researchers are now turning to, because why, exactly, some people don't cry is still not fully understood. If tears are so important for human bonding, are people who never cry perhaps less socially connected? That's exactly what preliminary research is finding, according to clinical psychologist Cord Benecke, a professor at the University of Kassel in Germany. He conducted intimate, therapy-style interviews with 120 individuals and looked to see if people who didn't cry were different from those who did. He found that they were.

"In general, they were not that closely bonded to others," Benecke says. "The noncrying people had a tendency to withdraw and described their relationship experiences as less connected." Tearless people also experienced more aggressive feelings, like rage, anger and disgust, than those who cried.

There are other reasons people don't cry. Some report losing their tears while taking medications such as antidepressants. Certain immune issues and psychological problems like post-traumatic stress disorder have also been linked to not crying. More research is needed to determine whether people who never tear up really are different from the rest of us.

Myth of the cleansing cry

So far, though crying appears to have interpersonal benefits, it's not necessarily unhealthy to never shed a tear. There's little evidence that crying comes with positive effects on health. Yet the perception persists that it's an emotional and physical detox, "like it's some kind of workout for your body," Rottenberg says. One analysis looked at articles in the media about crying—140 years' worth—and found that 94% described it as good for the mind and body and said holding back tears would result in the opposite. "It's kind of a fable," says Rottenberg. "There's not really any research to support that."

Also overblown is the idea that weeping always leads to feelings of relief. "There's an expectation that we feel better after we cry," says Randy Cornelius, a professor of psychology at Vassar College. "But the work that's been done on this indicates that, if anything, we don't feel good after we cry." When researchers show people a sad movie and measure their mood immediately afterward, the ones who cry are in worse moods than those who don't.

But other evidence does back the notion of the so-called good cry that leads to catharsis. One of the most important factors is giving the release enough time to sink in. When Vingerhoets and his colleagues showed people a tearjerker and measured their mood 90 minutes later instead of right after the movie, people who had cried were in a better mood than they had been before the film. Once the benefits of crying set in, he explains, it can be an effective way to recover from a strong bout of emotion. (Not surprisingly, how cathartic a cry is depends on whether people react well and whether the situation causing those tears is ameliorated.)

Modern crying research is still in its infancy, but the mysteries of tears—and the recent evidence that they're far more important than scientists once believed—drive Vingerhoets and the small cadre of tear researchers to keep at it. "Tears are of extreme relevance for human nature," points out Vingerhoets. "We cry because we need other people. So Darwin," he says with a laugh, "was totally wrong."

> *If tears are so important for human bonding, are people who never cry perhaps less socially connected?*

Natural Mood Changers

HOW SIX MAINSTAYS OF MODERN LIFE TWEAK OUR
NEUROCHEMISTRY—AND THE WAY WE FEEL

BY KATE ROCKWOOD

HUMANS HAVE LONG GRAVITATED TOWARD ACTIVITIES—BOTH
life-affirming and self-destructive—that make us feel good, even
if we don't know why. Now science has pulled back the curtain on
the fascinating ways in which a variety of factors, from booze to
workouts, impact our brains and emotions. Antidepressants are,
of course, the ultimate mood changers. The most commonly pre-
scribed ones are serotonin reuptake inhibitors, or SSRIs, which
work by blocking the brain's reabsorption of serotonin, so that more
of this feel-good substance is available. But even without a doctor's
Rx, people try to tweak their emotional states. The following natural
mood shifters play with our brain chemicals, for better or for worse.

Alcohol

It's an oft-traversed slippery slope: booze makes us feel good—until
it doesn't. That's because alcohol initially increases the amount of
dopamine in the nucleus accumbens, one of the brain's pleasure cen-
ters, and also releases opioid peptides such as endorphins (similar to
opiates). "Alcohol activates the brain reward system," says George
Koob, a neurobiologist who heads the National Institute on Alcohol Abuse and Alcoholism and has spent more than three decades
studying alcohol's impact.

But those pleasurable feelings disappear if drinking continues.
Whereas an occasional cocktail lights up this feel-good center, regular heavy consumption fries it. In fact, longtime drinkers lose the
dopamine boost and the opioid-peptide release, Koob says, no longer

getting that happiness payoff. That's not the only downside to chronic use. Besides harming the liver, in large quantities booze actually increases levels of cortisol, a hormone that is released in response to stress. Over time and with abuse, then, the same substance that creates happy hours can also leave people feeling miserable.

Marijuana

As with alcohol, cannabis's effect on the brain and emotions is complex. Pot users display a greater response when they view angry faces and a smaller response to happy faces, according to research by Lucy Troup, an assistant professor of psychology at Colorado State University who has spent two years measuring brain activity via electroencephalogram, or EEG, in chronic, moderate and non-users of cannabis. They're also less able to empathize with those emotions, suggesting that marijuana use may inhibit emotional processing at a deep level.

The jury is still out, however, on marijuana's overall impact. Troup is in the middle of another study focusing on pot's effect on mood disorders including depression and anxiety. "Psycho-pharmacologically, we still don't know how cannabis works," she says. The plant has 120 phytocannabinoids—chemical compounds that affect the brain's neurotransmitters—"and we don't know how they each interact with the others," Troup explains.

She points out that a person's response to cannabis may be largely genetic as well, which means emotional reactions vary. "We know that with post-traumatic stress disorder, marijuana either really helps or it pushes you over the edge," she says. Recent research has identified a variation of the AKT1 gene that makes people more susceptible to weed's mind-altering effects and even marijuana-induced psychosis.

The bottom line, according to Troup: pot is something of a wild card. "We don't yet have the science to back up marijuana for anxiety or depression," she says, "but it certainly does affect how the brain processes emotions."

Caffeine

We know that a jolt of caffeine wakes us up and helps us focus, but the stimulant also affects us in more complex ways. Caffeine stimulates the central nervous system in the brain, triggering the release of dopamine and serotonin as well as adrenaline and norepinephrine, the hormones involved in the body's fight-or-flight response. Down too many cups, and that hormonal surge will make you feel irritable and anxious.

Caffeine makes us feel alert by tricking our brains. Because it's structurally similar to adenosine—a neurotransmitter that causes us to feel tired—caffeine can bind to our brain's adenosine receptors and block the real thing from adhering, which stops us from feeling sleepy. Java drinkers have lower rates of depression, possibly because of caffeine's ability to bind to receptors that affect emotions. A 2011 study published in the *Archives of Internal Medicine* found that women who drank two to three cups per day were 15% less likely to develop depression than women who consumed one cup or less per day. Coffee drinkers also have a lower risk of suicide, according to other research.

But as with most substances, too much of a good thing can turn ugly. Downing too many cups can make you irritable and sleepless, and research has shown that caffeine can provoke panic attacks in people prone to anxiety.

You may feel miserable if you miss your daily cup, but caffeine is not addictive in the true biochemical sense of the term. It triggers a small increase in dopamine, a chemical in the brain that controls movement, motivation and emotions. But it's not a large enough surge to create significant, long-lasting changes. In contrast, a huge surge in dopamine—such as the one that occurs when someone takes methamphetamines or other addictive drugs—generates dramatic, lasting changes in the brain. That is what make a true addiction, unlike a caffeine habit, so difficult to overcome.

Orgasm

Even though the emotional impact of other drugs and chemicals is mixed, it's safe to say that an orgasm is a 100% positive mood booster, right? *Right?* Actually, no. "What's remarkable about orgasms is that they reliably induce mixed emotional states," says Nicole Prause, a Los Angeles–based neuroscientist who founded Liberos, a neuroscience company that studies arousal. "When people feel aroused, they report happiness and joy but also guilt and sometimes anger." Researchers aren't sure why, though it may be related to chemicals in the brain.

But overall, the big O is linked to positive moods. A study in the Netherlands found that in women, during sexual climax, the amygdala—the primitive part of your brain linked to vigilance and fear—deactivates. Sexual release quiets your brain and releases it from the tyranny of self-awareness.

At the same time, orgasm floods the brain's opioid receptors with endorphins and activates the hypothalamus, which excretes oxytocin, a hormone that encourages bonding. Prause is now researching whether orgasm might serve as a reset button for the brain, helping to disrupt obsessive thought patterns and treat depression, anxiety and obsessive-compulsive disorder.

Sugar

People have long joked that they are addicted to sugar—and now brain scans are confirming the similarities between sweeteners and highly addictive drugs. Sugar may be habit-forming because the substance induces the same neurochemical changes that occur with other drugs, according to a 2008 study published in the journal *Neuroscience & Biobehavioral Reviews*. Getting a sugar fix increases dopamine release in the nucleus accumbens—a key component in the brain's reward system—in much the same way that booze and drugs do. Over time, repeated sweets binges have the same dulling effect on dopamine receptors as chronic drug or alcohol abuse. That means that eventually you will need a larger hit (read: a second brownie) to feel that same thrill.

Eating a sugar-laden diet also hampers your brain's ability to learn and remember information, says Fernando Gomez-Pinilla, a professor of neurosurgery at UCLA: "What you eat affects how you think."

Exercise

Of all the external forces that affect your mood, exercise comes closest to being a panacea. Studies show that regular exercise can combat depression (even in people who do not respond well to antidepressants), prevent depression in the first place, ease stress, ward off cognitive decline and relieve emotional issues related to menopause.

Whew. Exercise is such a powerful tonic for our emotional state that some experts consider it a legitimate treatment option for people with milder forms of depression.

Experts are still unwinding the many ways working out benefits the brain. University of British Columbia scientists found that in elderly women with mild cognitive decline, regular aerobic exercise increases the size of the hippocampus, the brain region associated with verbal memory and learning. Other studies show that exercise boosts the volume of the prefrontal cortex and medial temporal cortex, which govern thinking and memory.

And that's not all. Physical activity actually creates new brain cells, or neurons, that are more impervious to stress than regular neurons. A Princeton University study showed that mice that ran for six weeks had a large increase in new neurons in the ventral hippocampus (a brain region shown to regulate anxiety) that release GABA, a neurotransmitter that quiets an excitable brain. As a result, reports Elizabeth Gould, the neuroscientist who led the study, it's not a stretch to say that exercise modifies the human brain to be more resilient to stress.

As for "runner's high": it's real. German scientists have shown that, in mice, that rush is related not to endorphins but to an increase in the level of endocannabinoids in the bloodstream. Working out spikes what is basically the body's naturally occurring cannabis, triggering a state of euphoria and relaxation.

> *Exercise is such a powerful tonic for our emotional state that some consider it a treatment option for depression.*

PART TWO

Connect with Others

"I've learned that people will forget what you said, people will forget what you did, but people will never forget how you made them feel."

—MAYA ANGELOU

Are Emotions Contagious?

YES, YOU CAN CATCH A FRIEND'S FEAR OR A CO-WORKER'S ANGER. THEIR JOY CAN RUB OFF ON YOU TOO

BY ALEXANDRA SIFFERLIN

SEVERAL YEARS AGO, ELAINE HATFIELD, A PROFESSOR OF PSY-chology at the University of Hawaii, realized that she kept feeling uncomfortable around a fellow faculty member. Though they worked well together and she considered the colleague a friend, she walked away from their conversations feeling insufficient and, frankly, stupid. Hatfield brought up the issue with her husband, Richard Rapson, a professor of history also at the university. What was wrong with her that she felt so anxious and self-doubting after spending time with this prickly co-worker?

"My god," her husband responded. "He's uncomfortable around women!" To Rapson, his wife's unease had an obvious source—her colleague's emotional state in the presence of the opposite sex. "I realized it wasn't me," says Hatfield, noting that the colleague did often appear to be quite anxious. "I was feeling badly that I couldn't make him feel better."

Hatfield had fallen victim to a cultural phenomenon that she would later become most known for studying: emotional contagion. Similar to the way people can pass the common cold around, Hatfield and other psychology experts have shown that people also spread their emotional states. "We catch all the basic emotions," she says. "Love, joy, fear and sadness. People who are likely to catch each other's emotions are sensitive observers."

There's a wealth of research to support emotional contagion as a legitimate occurrence, and it's likely that plenty of us can attest to experiencing it in day-to-day life. For instance, we might feel bummed after spending time with a colleague who complains all the time, whereas we feel rejuvenated after grabbing coffee with a close, enthusiastic friend. A 2008 study reported that when a nearby friend is happy, happiness can spread among that person's social group and even increase your own happiness by up to 25%. That means, however, that negative emotions can spread widely as well.

But how exactly does that happen? Psychologists generally agree on a few principles of emotional contagion. For one, people are constantly reading each other's moods, even though we may not realize it. Decades ago, social psychologist Phil Shaver revealed that people can identify around 135 different emotions, and we often do so rather quickly. When we interact with others, we partake in what's referred to as a mimicry, in which we mimic what other people are doing. This might mean that we frown if the person we are conversing with is frowning or adjust our posture to synchronize with theirs. People also tend to experience feedback from their own facial expressions and body language. Some studies suggest that smiling or frowning may actually make people feel better or worse. Basically, we pick up each other's nonverbal cues and, in some cases, "catch" each other's moods.

Why we feel others' pain

There's likely an evolutionary advantage to reading one another's emotions. Family members' ability to pick up on how their relatives are feeling is important for well-being, says Hatfield. For example, parents' ability to bond with a newborn and understand when their child is hungry or sick can be critical for the baby's survival in the early days. It's

When a nearby friend is happy, that happiness can spread and increase your own happiness by 25%.

also essential for maintaining relationships. That's great when you detect a happy mood, of course, but not so great if you absorb someone's anger or sadness. For people who are especially receptive to negative emotions, this phenomenon can take a toll on mental health.

That's why some researchers argue that communities, especially workplaces (where many people spend most of their days), need to be cognizant of the powerful impact emotions have on culture. "It's important for businesses to be aware of emotional contagion, because there's voluminous literature from more than a quarter of a century showing emotions influence workplace outcomes in employee attitudes and productivity," says Sigal Barsade, a professor of management at the Wharton School of the University of Pennsylvania who has spent years studying how emotional contagion can play out in the workplace. "Emotional contagion is ubiquitous, and our studies show that people don't realize it's happening."

Barsade's research over more than 10 years has shown that emotional culture can greatly influence employee satisfaction or burnout and potentially even how well a business does. In one 16-month study of a long-term healthcare facility, Barsade and her colleagues found that people working in units that had a culture of companionate love—affection, caring and compassion that employees feel and express toward one another—had fewer missed days among their employees, more teamwork, more job satisfaction and less burnout. That culture had other positive ripple effects too: employees did their jobs better, and family members of patients in their units were more likely to report higher levels of satisfaction in the facility.

Hatfield and other researchers have explored how emotional investment taxes people who work in notoriously emotionally draining situations, such as caregivers and therapists. One 2014 study of 730 nurses in a hospital found that those who said they were

Do other people's moods tend to rub off on you? You may be particularly susceptible to emotional contagion.

motivated by their desire to help people were more likely to burn out faster than people who said they liked the work itself.

But how can we use emotional contagion to improve community or company culture? Cultivating a positive emotional experience needs to start at the top. "The primary mechanism for creating a healthy emotional culture is through leaders," Barsade notes. "How did the leader walk in this morning? Are they upbeat, or is the weight of the world on their shoulders?"

Of course, a community culture, whether it's at a startup or a nursing home, built solely on love and care can have its downsides. People may feel like it's not acceptable to call out a co-worker for slacking or have a necessary confrontation with a manager. To combat that, Barsade says, some organizations have developed emotional cultures that balance each other out. For instance, in a study

of firefighters, Barsade found that members talked about having a lighthearted workplace where pranks were common, along with an atmosphere of companionate love, where the firefighters were fiercely loyal and supportive of one another. "If you work in a place with companionate love, it shouldn't be that you can get away with everything," says Barsade. "But you will get feedback in a way that's respectful and caring."

Reaping the rewards

On a personal level, there are ways that people can benefit from the positive effects of emotional contagion while simultaneously protecting themselves from the negative ones. Hatfield says she recommends that people try to gain insight into why a person is behaving in a certain way or feeling they way they are. "That doesn't mean approving of a monster or

Getting silly with friends isn't just a diversion—it's a smart strategy for emotional health.

letting yourself get pushed around," she says. "But simply understanding them helps."

Letting go of the things we can't change is important too. "If you are a parent, maybe you can alter your child's behavior," says Hatfield. "But for adults, you are a fool to take responsibility when you have no power. Acknowledge the power of contagion, then remind yourself: don't take too much in."

Simply knowing that emotional contagion exists is another good way to inoculate yourself against some of its more negative side effects, says Barsade. In a given situation, understanding that you might be feeling down because you were empathizing with a sad friend can be helpful. Some people are more susceptible to emotional contagion than others, and acknowledging that tendency in yourself can help you better navigate touchy situations with others. It's a tactic Barsade uses herself as someone who is more likely to catch whatever emotions are going around. "I am the type of person who cries during commercials," she admits.

How to spread the love

Being conscious of your own mood is also important. The spread of emotions goes both ways: just as other people can alter your mood, you affect how others are feeling. Your nonverbal cues of anger, like crossed arms or eye rolling, can infect friends and family.

That said, it is hard to put on a happy face when you're feeling frustrated or blue. To combat that, Barsade suggests employing what's called "deep acting" rather than "surface acting." Surface acting is half-heartedly wishing someone a good day, whereas deep acting is trying to get yourself to a place where you truly mean your words, and making eye contact rather than avoiding another's gaze. Of course, combating negative mood transfer can also be done directly. When the need arises, Barsade recommends having a conversation with the person who is getting you down.

On the other hand, spending time with people who lift your mood is worth your while. After all, happiness is also contagious, and it is one feeling nobody minds catching.

SHE FEELS, HE FEELS

ARE WOMEN MORE EMOTIONAL? ARE MEN QUICKER TO ANGER?
THE SEXES FEEL THE SAME EMOTIONS BUT SOMETIMES ACT
ON THEM DIFFERENTLY, THANKS TO NURTURE AND NATURE

BY EMILY BARONE

WOMEN

There may be some truth to the stereotype: **on average, women cry more than men,** in part because of hormonal differences between the sexes. Women are also more likely than men to have suicidal thoughts, according to the U.S. Department of Health and Human Services.

Women use words to get what they want while preserving social harmony. **They may be slower to act out of anger than men** because their orbital frontal cortex (the brain's emotional control center) is relatively larger than their amygdala (which registers anger), per a study in the journal *Cerebral Cortex*.

Women are about twice as likely as men to suffer from generalized anxiety, according to 2016 research published in *Brain and Behavior*. **Women are also about twice as likely as men to have specific phobias, such as toward heights or snakes**, according to *Behaviour Research and Therapy*.

University of Montreal researchers found that **women are better than men at reading facial expressions and tone of voice** (which may help with fostering relationships). Women pick up subtle signs of sadness 90% of the time, whereas men pick up on such signs 40% of the time, notes Louann Brizendine in her book *The Female Brain*.

MEN

Men are less likely than women to express vulnerability, in part because of societal norms. This is one reason only a third of mental-health outpatient visits are by men, according to the American Psychological Association. **Men are about four times as likely as women to die from suicide.**

Multiple studies have found a link between testosterone and aggression, likely because testosterone activates our brain's emotion center, the amygdala. While men and women feel the same amount and intensity of anger, **men are more likely to assault the target of their anger physically.**

In relationships, in sports or at work, men display less fear and are primed to fight when their territory is challenged, says neuropsychiatrist Louann Brizendine. **Men are driven by thrill even when facing danger**. The brain system associated with self-control doesn't fully mature in boys until they are in their 20s.

Men show caring by offering solutions to alleviate stress or sadness. Their brains dial down empathy and amp up analysis. When men fall in love, their brains light up most in areas associated with visual processing, including one linked to sexual arousal, found research by biological anthropologist Helen Fisher.

SADNESS

ANGER

FEAR AND ANXIETY

LOVE

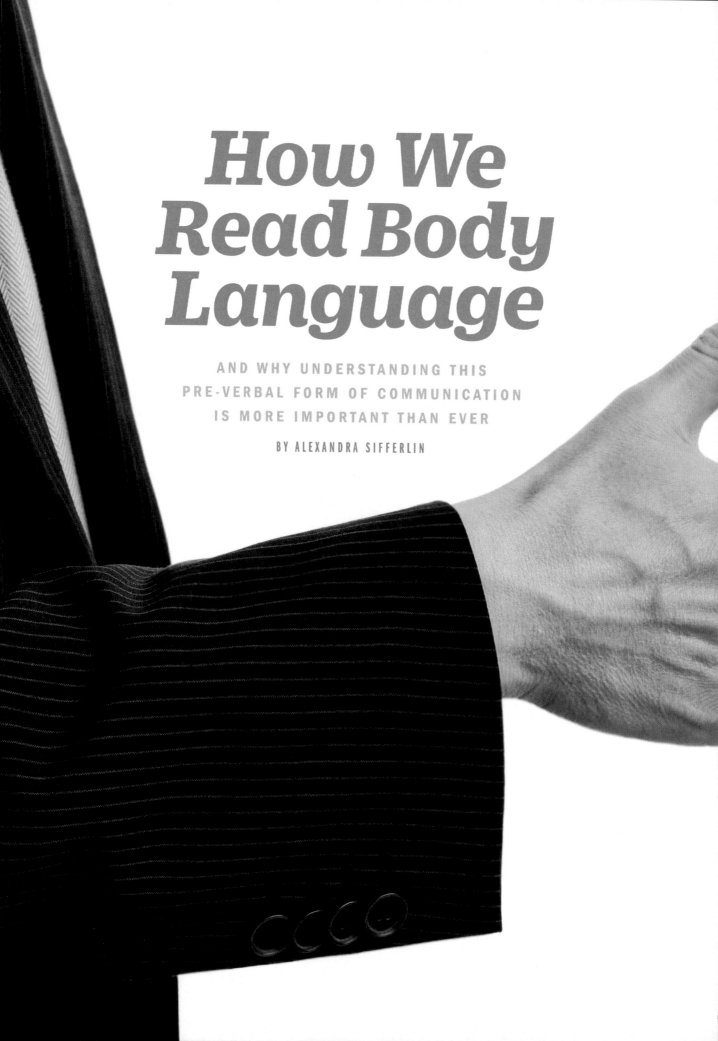

How We Read Body Language

AND WHY UNDERSTANDING THIS
PRE-VERBAL FORM OF COMMUNICATION
IS MORE IMPORTANT THAN EVER

BY ALEXANDRA SIFFERLIN

IN MODERN SOCIETY, THERE ARE AN ENDLESS number of ways to communicate. We have email, texting, Twitter, Snapchat—the list goes on. Yet these contemporary modes of communication lack one of humanity's oldest languages. No, it's not speech. Evolutionarily speaking, speech is believed to have entered human discourse rather late in the game. Rather, one of the most established ways to convey information and emotions is through postures, gestures and eye movements—otherwise known as body language.

Some of the earliest documentation of the importance of body language came from Europe during the Renaissance, when researchers tried to understand which facial expressions and gestures signaled various emotions. Later, Charles Darwin would argue that people inherit the facial expressions they use in daily life. To what extent body language is a universal language, and how nuances depend on community and context, remain debated. But what's clear is that humans have unconsciously used body language to read one another and communicate for centuries, if not longer. Today we often describe people's emotional states through their posture and body positioning. Someone might have a "stiff upper lip" or "give us the cold shoulder." These nonverbal gestures and expressions are actually, according to research, not just valuable ways to share information but often critical for successful social interactions.

Take the findings of Albert Mehrabian, currently a professor emeritus of psychology at UCLA, who is considered one of the fathers of modern body-language science. In the 1960s, he estimated that depending on the circumstance, the delivery of a message is 7% verbal, 38% vocal—which means tone of voice and other sounds—and 55% nonverbal. Mehrabian's breakdown specifically applied to situations where people's actions and their words do not align. Let's say you're giving a presentation to a crowded room about a topic you don't actually care that much about. According to Mehrabian, it's highly likely that the people listening to you will pick up on those cues and pay much more attention to what your body language is saying than the words you're delivering. Why is that important? Understanding how this effect may help us, or sabotage us, is a useful tool for everything from partner bonding to success in the workplace.

Getting fluent in body language

There are obvious reasons body language is important. A parent's ability to understand an infant or child's needs may have broad implications for survival, and picking up on a friend or partner's emotional state can be critical for relationships. But researchers still have a lot of questions when it comes to how we detect these clues and what we can glean from them.

Most recently, social scientists are gaining a greater understanding of how humans use their entire bodies to process and display emotions. "There has been much more progress in the study of face perception in the study of body language," says Alexander Todorov, a professor of psychology at Princeton University and the author of *Face Value: The Irresistible Influence of First Impressions*. "Because our attention is often focused on the face, we underweight the importance of body gestures, but there is a lot of meaningful information to be extracted from these gestures."

In a 2012 study published in the journal *Science*, Todorov and fellow researchers at Hebrew University of Jerusalem and New York University asked men and women to look at photos and determine whether the people in the pictures were experiencing feelings of loss, pain or victory from their facial expressions, their body language or both. In some cases the facial expression and the body language appeared to be exhibiting different emotions. In four different experiments, the

People appear to process information with their full body, rather than simply their mind.

Heightened emotions are apparent in the body poses and gestures in Vicente Juan Masip's *The Last Supper*.

study participants were much more likely to guess the correct emotion based on body language, either alone or with facial expressions, than when they had only facial features to work with. That study challenged years of thinking that a person's emotions show predominantly in the face.

"Body language is important, because it provides context for interpreting the meaning of facial expressions," says Todorov. "Generally, facial expressions are much more ambiguous than we think. However, because the context, including body language, helps us disambiguate the meaning of these expressions, we are rarely aware of their ambiguity."

Another interesting discovery in the past 10 years is that people appear to process information with their full body, rather than simply their mind, and sometimes this processing of information has physical cues. In a 2010 study, researchers from the University of Aberdeen in Scotland found that when they asked study volunteers to think about the future, many people leaned forward slightly, and people who were asked to reflect on the past leaned back. "When we talk about time, we often use spatial metaphors like 'I'm looking forward to seeing you' or 'I'm reflecting back on the past,'" said study author Lynden

K. Miles, a senior lecturer in the school of psychology, when the study came out. "It was pleasing to us that we could take an abstract concept such as time and show that it was manifested in body movements."

Today, by observing synchrony, Miles continues to study how the body physically adapts to situations. "When two people are walking along, they will spontaneously coordinate their footsteps," he says. "We've shown that when that happens, people get along better, trust more and remember each other better." Miles believes that we read each other's body movements and unconsciously try to mimic them as a way to spur affiliation and friendliness and achieve positive bonds with other people.

What is more revealing, the face or the body?

But just how well can we actually read other people based on their body language? Experts differ on that answer. There are plenty of researchers and psychology experts who argue that our own body language can help us, say, when meeting new people or landing a job interview. Common body-language features often cited as simple ways to exude confidence include using a firm handshake, making eye

Interviewing for a job? Making eye contact and mirroring the posture of the hiring manager may give you a leg up.

contact and maintaining good posture.

Often people apply their knowledge of body language to public figures, especially leaders. It's a much more common phenomenon today than it was during prior decades, when Americans relied on newspaper articles, letters or radio to get messages from government officials, including the president. That's changed dramatically with the advent of television and cable news. During the 2016 presidential election, several media articles claimed to break down the body-language dynamics of the debates between candidates Donald Trump and Hillary Clinton. In some cases, journalists even watched the debates on mute, arguing that Trump was aggressive, with "almost manic hand and arm gestures," whereas Clinton appeared in control, smiling and laughing throughout. By all body-language suggestions, Clinton won the debates, and early polling appeared to agree.

But whether a person can truly claim to know and understand the inner dealings of another human simply by observing them from afar may be unlikely. Three years ago, the use of body-language readings by Transportation Security Administration employees received criticism. For years, the agency paid millions to train behavior-detection officers to read facial expressions as well as other body-language cues to identify potential terrorists at airports. A review of the TSA's budget for such trainings came under fire, with some critics arguing that identifying a liar through his or her facial expressions is much harder than believed, and that data suggests most people are not great at it. Some people may have a good poker face, too. In 2006 two

able or off-putting, says Miles. For instance, someone who doesn't recognize or respect other people's personal space and boundaries may be a red flag. "If I am the only person on the bus and you sit right next to me, that becomes awkward compared to if it's the only space available," he says. "I think something like personal space is an important metric of social interaction." Although this violation of personal space could be nothing more than a benign misreading of social cues, it could also be an intentional action to elicit discomfort or even fear.

Keeping in mind that we are constantly reading body language, and that other people are interpreting ours at the same time, is also helpful. Princeton's Todorov has spent years studying the science behind first impressions and learning that people are often wrong in the snap judgments they make of others very quickly after meeting. Our minds are also forming these quick assessments all the time, though we are rarely aware that the process is happening. "First impressions are quite automatic and feel more like perception rather than thought," he says. "The best we can do is to be aware of the potential biases of these impressions." Remembering that we can be fooled by body language, or incorrectly interpret someone's facial expressions, especially upon first meeting or among people we don't know very well, may prevent us from making bias-based judgments.

But if body language can sometimes be deceiving, there may be ways to use it to our advantage. Some researchers argue that by consciously changing our body language, we can have a positive effect on our personal outcomes, whether it's nailing a presentation at work or making a good impression on new acquaintances. Adopting a confident posture (leaning in, taking a wide stance), for example, may actually make people feel more confident and useful, some studies suggest. Whether our body positioning affects our mind and self-esteem in a potent way is still an area of active research, but experts suggest giving it a shot. Striking a power pose or giving a self-assured handshake may just be an easy way to put your best foot forward.

psychologists reviewed about 200 studies on the subject and found that people correctly identified liars less than 50% of the time, and that the accuracy rate was even lower in studies in which people could not hear what a person was saying and were reading body language alone.

"If there were some body movements that were more informative than others, then I think people would become aware and start to control them," says Miles. "I think if we started to look for parts of body language that were more informative, we might be headed down the wrong track."

Are first impressions valid?
Still, there are things we can learn from body language that are helpful—like picking up on certain actions that might be uncomfort-

Go Ahead, Cry at Work

CORPORATE CULTURE HAS LONG IGNORED THE FACT THAT WE CAN'T CHECK OUR FEELINGS AT THE OFFICE DOOR. WHY IT'S HIGH TIME TO GET RATIONAL ABOUT EMOTIONS IN THE WORKPLACE

BY ANNE KREAMER

I WAS A 37-YEAR-OLD SENIOR VICE PRESIDENT IN CHARGE OF THE consumer-products-and-publishing division at Nickelodeon, the children's cable channel, in my office celebrating with a few colleagues the announcement of a huge, groundbreaking deal with Sony to create and market home videos of our hit shows, such as *Rugrats* and *Ren & Stimpy*.

The phone rang. My assistant shouted, "Oh, man—it's Sumner! On Line 1!" Sumner Redstone, that is, then the chairman and majority owner of Viacom Inc., the parent company of Nickelodeon. During my three years at the company, Redstone had rarely spoken to me and had never phoned. How generous of him, I thought, to take the time and make the effort to thank me personally.

Now, that's a good boss. This was it: my moment of glory.

I picked up the phone, anticipating a congratulatory exchange about what a great job my team had done. Instead, Redstone, then nine days shy of 70, started screaming at me. "Do you know what you've done?" he raged. I was absolutely blindsided. I hunched over the telephone and turned away from my colleagues.

In spite of healthy media coverage, including a positive article in the *Wall Street Journal*, the public announcement of the

Sony deal had failed to move Viacom's stock price—and Redstone was livid about it. I could practically feel his spittle frothing out of my telephone receiver. I sat there, crushed at being so undervalued for my many months of hard work, mortified to feel tears welling up while co-workers were in my office and angry at the injustice of being singled out for abuse. But I couldn't express what I was feeling. I believed that to do so would have been professional suicide. Ninety seconds after I'd picked up the phone, Redstone, without a goodbye, hung up.

The tears that had welled up during the call began spilling out as I tried to process the information. Fearing a total meltdown, I avoided saying anything about what had just happened, managing, perhaps, to force out an uninspired "Great job, everyone! I am suddenly so tired I can hardly keep my head up. How about we call it a day and all go home?" I stayed in that job for another 2½ years, but two decades later, I still smart at the memory of that moment.

Instead of avoiding emotion, we need to become more rational about it.

I have since learned from several former colleagues at Nickelodeon that I was not at all unique in being on the receiving end of the chairman's anger. I have also learned that I too made a co-worker cry, when I shot down his presentation in a monthly strategy meeting. I'm not proud of that moment and wish I'd found a better way to get my criticism across. But the goal of organizations should not be to eliminate the expression of emotions at work, which is what our dominant management paradigm tries to do.

In the binary shorthand we use to compartmentalize modern life, we think of home as the realm of emotion and work as the place where rationality rules—a tidy distinction that crumbles in the face of experience. As management scholar Blake Ashforth has written, it is a "convenient fiction that organizations are cool arenas for dispassionate thought and action." In fact, in the workplace we are bombarded by emotions—our own and everyone else's. Neuroscientists have demon-strated over and over in empirical ways just how integral emotion is in all aspects of our lives, including our work. But since companies have generally avoided the subject, there are no clear protocols about emotional expression in the office.

The only instance in which we acknowledge emotion is when doing so is seen as obviously beneficial, both personally and professionally. In the late 1990s, psychologist Daniel Goleman identified four components of what he called emotional intelligence—self-awareness, self-management, social awareness and relationship management—and presented a number of case studies showing how organizations that operate in emotionally intelligent ways can be more competitive. Over the past decade, a diffuse notion of emotional intelligence has been widely disseminated. "What I hear you saying is . . ." has become a 21st-century executive cliché.

But we're still largely clueless about how to display and react to more commonplace emotions such as anger, fear and anxiety, so we handicap ourselves, trying to check our human side at the office door. "Traditionally, organizational behavior has only examined things people could easily see or report," says Sigal Barsade, a professor at the University of Pennsylvania's Wharton School. "But I think we've missed an entire level of analysis, which is unconscious. If I asked a man who gets cut off in traffic on his way to work and then has to make a strategic decision in a 9 a.m. meeting if the anger he felt in any way influenced his decision, he'd answer, 'Absolutely not,' when we have concrete evidence that it would. This lack of awareness can be insidious."

Instead of avoiding emotion, we need to become more rational about it. This is not to suggest that being embarrassed, frustrated or upset at work is inappropriate but rather that when colleagues show emotion, we should learn to interpret why those particular feelings were triggered and understand what happens on a social, psychological and even

Power bawl: Tears in the office are more likely to be triggered by frustration or anger than sadness.

biological level as well as get to the bottom of our prejudices and reactions. Had I known, at the time of my Nickelodeon crying episode, the biochemical purpose of my tears (nature's reset button), I would have appreciated that they didn't necessarily signal unprofessionalism or weakness. And I would have grasped that emotionality at the workplace is not a female issue—men and women are equally driven by it, even if the emotions are sometimes expressed differently.

Emotions 101

Part of the reason emotions at work present such a challenge is that, evolutionarily speaking, our responses have not caught up with our environment. At its most basic, an emotion is an automatic physiological response. We do not get angry and then have our blood pressure rise; rather, our blood pressure rises in response to some threatening stimulus. For our ancestors, it was essential to survival

to go on high alert before assessing whether the stick in the road was really just a stick or a venomous snake.

At work, knowing what to make of our emotions is much more complicated. Real or perceived assaults on our egos, our social standing or our value to the organization are far more subjective threats. And yet we react to psychological threats with a hardwired biological response. It's this ancient-versus-modern struggle—our inability to step back and see what's happening for what it is—that underlies our difficulty with handling emotion at work. Then there is the thick overlay of personal and social inhibitions, biases and stereotypes surrounding the expression of emotions.

To learn more about all these forces, I partnered with J. Walter Thompson, a major ad agency, to conduct two national surveys. In the first, the Emotional Incidents in the Workplace Survey, we asked nine questions

One poll found younger women are more likely than men to be angry at work but less apt to say it's acceptable.

of a random sample of more than 700 Americans, equally divided by gender, representing the full range of occupational levels and economic sectors. For instance, what did a respondent feel before, during and after crying, getting angry or feeling despondent at work? Were those emotions related to the job? We also tried to get a sense of how people regard co-workers who express emotion.

We found that frustration was the most commonly experienced emotion. Almost half of all respondents reported having become upset because they thought a co-worker wasn't doing his or her job. Sixty percent of all workers had seen their boss get angry at someone during the past year. And 41% of women had cried at work, compared with only 9% of men. Yet for both men and women, whether or not they had cried at work made no difference in how much they reported they liked their job.

Differences between the physiologies of men's and women's tears explain, in part, the greater number of female criers on the job. In general, women cry almost four times as of-

ten as men, according to biochemist William Frey. Women's tear ducts are anatomically different from men's, resulting in a larger volume of tears. In fact, often when men cry, tears do not fall down their cheeks.

But for women, crying is far less disruptive at work than the shame and guilt that follow. Crying stimulates the production of the feel-good neurotransmitter dopamine and restores emotional equilibrium. But we found that in spite of the cathartic physiological benefits, women who cry at work feel rotten afterward, as if they've failed a feminism test. In contrast, the male criers in our survey tended to report that after their crying, their minds felt sharper, the future seemed brighter, and they felt more physically relaxed and in control. In short: according to our survey, women, who have a biological predisposition to cry more, feel worse after crying at work, while men feel better.

And women are harder on others who cry, especially other women: 43% of the women in our study, versus 32% of the men, considered people who cry at work "unstable," which sounds like a serious character flaw or mental disorder. Rather than harshly judging themselves and others for something that's a biological fact—tears are, after all, similar to a hiccup, sneeze or burp—wouldn't it be far better for women to instead focus on what stressors our tears might be revealing?

Workplace weeping is far more likely to be triggered by anger and frustration than by sadness. Women reported feeling angry at work more than men did, especially younger women (ages 18–44). Men were more likely to express their anger, however, which suggests that they feel safer in doing so; in our survey, 42% of young men felt that anger is an effective management tool (as Sumner Redstone clearly did), versus only 23% of young women.

When women do cut loose, they then experience greater distress about having done so, which makes their anger backfire internally. (According to social psychologist Carol Tavris, your expression of anger must restore your sense of control over the situation in order for it to be effective.) But if women feel conflicted about expressing anger, it's with good reason—their anger is almost invariably perceived and interpreted differently than men's.

In 2007, two business-school researchers, Victoria Brescoll of Yale and Eric Uhlmann of Northwestern, conducted three studies in which participants watched videos of actors pretending to apply for jobs, sometimes showing anger or sadness and sometimes not, and then assigned jobs and salaries to the make-believe new hires. Not only were women judged to be worse employees when they expressed anger, but also, angry men were actually judged to be better hires than non-angry men.

Additionally, a woman's anger was attributed to her personality—"she is an angry person"; "she is out of control"—while men's emotional reactions tended to be seen as justifiable—"the work was shoddy" or "the report sucked." In this context, it's no wonder that more than 50% of women reported being angry at work during the past year—for the moment, there is simply no socially appropriate way for women to express legitimate anger in the workplace.

And there needs to be, because emotions have as much impact on our work performance as cognitive brain functions do. Studies by Antonio Damasio at the University of Southern California's Brain and Creativity Institute and others have demonstrated that without emotion, it is impossible to make decisions. Real emotional intelligence is more than being sensitive or nice, more than understanding how to read the mood of a conference room or having insight into whether a colleague is more analytical or expressive in her approach to problem-solving. The workplace has never been more diverse than it is today, the boundaries between the personal and the professional never so blurry. The ability to not only envision alternative responses to a given situation but also understand that there are entire invisible galaxies of salient emotional facts behind almost every exchange on the job is not just more possible than ever; it's more urgent.

> *Emotions have as much impact on our work performance as cognitive brain functions do.*

There are payoffs, personal and professional. In our study, 69% of respondents felt that when someone gets emotional in the workplace, it makes the person seem more human, and a whopping 88% of all workers (93% of women and 83% of men) felt that being sensitive to others' emotions at work is an asset. Emotions are who we are. As management consultant Erika Andersen (author of *Being Strategic* and also my sister-in-law) says, "No one wants to cry at work. But if you say to yourself, 'I know people will sometimes get overwhelmed, and if that happens one or two times a year, can I handle that?'—well, the answer is, 'Yes, of course I can handle that.' Crying at work is transformative and can open the door to change."

Adapted from *It's Always Personal*, by Anne Kreamer. Copyright © 2011 by Anne Kreamer. Published by Random House, a division of Penguin Random House, LLC.

Secrets to Mental Toughness

WHAT A CIA OPERATIVE, A GREEN BERET
AND AN ER DOCTOR CAN TEACH US ABOUT
KEEPING COOL UNDER PRESSURE

BY DAN BOVA

HI. CAN I TELL YOU ABOUT THE TIME I LOST MY DAMN MIND?

Those who know me would say that I'm a pretty calm, cool and collected guy. But one day, about two years ago, I was none of those things.

There were three key ingredients that resulted in a recipe for disaster: (1) me, stressed out after having just been laid off; (2) a grocery-store customer-service desk worker with a severe allergy to providing service to customers; and (3) a seriously funky-smelling chicken.

After opening a package of chicken that smelled like it was packed with fish heads, I brought it back to the store to get a refund. I calmly (I swear) explained the situation to the woman behind the customer-service counter. After hearing my tale of "whoa!" she sniffed at me (not the chicken) and pointed at the sell-by date. "This chicken is expired," she said.

"No, no," I explained. "The sell-by date is today. It should still be good."

"It means to sell it before today," she replied. "It means that today it is expired. We wouldn't sell this in our store."

Only they did sell it in their store. To me. I asked to speak with the manager. "I am the manager," she informed me.

Sensing defeat, I started to leave, but something about the way the automatic doors flung open seemed to say: "So long, loser!" I'd been unceremoniously shown the door when I got laid off from my job a few weeks before, and at that moment, the Scotch tape and glue that were holding my sanity together broke. I spun back around.

"So you're telling me you don't sell anything today that is labeled to sell today?" I asked.

"That's right," she said.

That's when I stomped to the meat section and grabbed an armful of ground-beef packages stamped with that day's sell-by date. I stomped back to the customer-service desk like a deranged Bobby Flay in the weirdest episode of *Iron Chef* ever and dropped the pile onto her desk. "So you're either selling rotten meat in this store or the sell-by date means to sell it today. So which is it?" My entire body was trembling.

Without even looking at me, she pushed a few buttons on her register and handed me my victory: $11.34. I turned around in triumph and met the eyes of the next people in line. I saw some fear, but mostly pity. The automatic doors opened up again, this time as if to say, "Looks like someone could use a hug."

Know your plan B

Hurling meat at people is not normal behavior for me, and although we've never met, I'm going to guess that it isn't normal for you either. But we've all had those "freaking the freak out" moments. You're in a yelling match at a red light with some jerk who cut you off, or you're melting down because you're trying to get out the door for a meeting and water is gushing out of your kitchen sink, your kids won't get dressed for school, and the dog just yakked on the living-room rug.

So how do we keep from snapping? To find out, I spoke with real experts—a Green Beret, a CIA operative and an ER doctor—to find out how they keep levelheaded in moments that have even higher stakes than a ruined rug or $11 worth of spoiled chicken.

Drew Dwyer, a former Marine and CIA operative, knows a little bit about intense situations. During his 10-year run with the agency, he has been sent on high-risk missions that involve rescuing hostages and buying back missiles sold to Afghan rebels in the 1980s. Had I had his training, I surely would have approached my foul-fowl incident differently.

First mistake: I had no real plan if things didn't go my way. "One way to reduce the potential for losing your cool is to plan for the worst," says Dwyer. "Nothing ever goes the way you planned it, so you need to think of contingencies. The military calls it PACE: primary, alternate, contingency, emergency. When the primary plan goes out the door, you're on to the next one. When things go sideways, your heart rate jumps, and people tend to start moving and thinking too fast, making increasingly bad decisions as you get more and more agitated. PACE helps take that out of the equation."

> "One way to reduce the potential for losing your cool is to plan for the worst."

Asking your boss for a raise? Want to talk to your son's soccer coach about his lack of playing time? You don't want to walk in cold into situations where there is a big potential for unfavorable results and escalating emotions. Thinking it through ("if he says this, I'll say this") can help preserve your sanity in the moment. But even just reminding yourself that "this might not go how I want it to" will help avoid having embarrassing shock responses.

My second error was that I didn't have my head clear for the mission at hand. I might have had a bag of rotten chicken, but my lack of employment was what was really making me sick to my stomach. "When on a military mission, they call it 'being in the red,' " Dwyer says. "If you're leaving the gates of Kandahar, you don't want to have an argument with your girlfriend or bills you owe on your mind. If you let emotions from an unrelated issue bleed into what's right in front of you, it can cloud your judgment and lead to bad mistakes." So try to compartmentalize. The electrician just called to tell you it's going to cost eight times as much as he quoted to install those lights? Don't let it rain craziness in your brain as you walk into a meeting with important business clients. They have nothing to do with overpriced sconces.

Get tunnel vision

OK, so those techniques could help when you know you are heading into a confrontation, but what about that unexpected late-for-work-uncooperative-kids-exploding-sink-puking-dog scenario? How do you hold it together? I asked Catherine Jamin, chief of service at the Ronald O. Perelman Department of Emergency Medicine at NYU Langone.

"When things get very overwhelming, it is always good to step back and hit the reset button," explains Jamin. "Whether it is on a shift at work or at home or the two worlds are colliding, I take a few deep breaths and rethink my priorities: what has to happen first and what comes after that, and so on."

In the ER, prioritizing—called triage—is vitally important. Someone who is coding (meaning the heart stopped) needs instant treatment, whereas someone with a herniated disc may be in pain, but time is not of the essence. Although hospitals use a numeric system called the Emergency Severity Index that puts emergencies on a scale of 1 to 5 (1 being most severe), Jamin told me that ER staff generally break it down into two groups: critical and not critical.

So in the case of the terrible, horrible, no good, very bad morning, you'll want to stop and think: What do I need to do first? Turn off the water main before you have a flood. The dog puke can wait.

Also remember that although you may feel this is all happening to you, there are often other people around you that you can delegate tasks to. Do that—and in the most even-keeled voice as possible.

Calm, Jamin says, is contagious. "As the team leader in the ER, you need to keep the room calm and under control. Speaking your thoughts out loud can keep you calm and keep those around you calm."

But what about when no one (i.e., the kids on the couch) is listening? "I have three young girls, and I think I've learned to choose my battles," explains Jamin. "In medicine and in dealing with home stuff, the trick is figuring out what you can let go. If my daughter doesn't want to wear the clothes I laid out for her, is it worth getting upset about, or are there more important things to focus on?"

Build your mental muscle

Having served in the U.S. Army for more than 25 years, Green Beret Sergeant Major (retired) Karl Erickson says that the key to being mentally strong is being physically strong as well. "You have to get off your butt and exercise. Get that body in shape, and the mind will follow," he says. "The body has physical reactions to stress. Your heart rate tends to skyrocket. So by exercising, you're training your heart to deal with stress. That's why in the military if we spend a day on the shooting range, we end a session with a stress test. It's all about teaching your mind and body to function while that heart is racing."

Erickson also believes in having a plan B. "Get in the habit of asking yourself, 'If something bad were to happen right now, what would I do?'" he says. "It doesn't matter if you are standing on line for coffee or at the movies or at work. And it doesn't have to be a crazy action-hero plan. Just knowing where the exit is can give you a lifesaving jump-start if something were to happen."

And if you forget to do any of this, all of the experts agree that you should imagine you are in a $125 yoga class and focus on your breathing. "Humans typically take 12 to 20 breaths a minute," says Erickson. "People under pressure sometimes hold their breath or turn into panting dogs, which will make you pass out or hyperventilate. Neither of those are useful."

A final note: find a personal mantra that works for you. Boss driving you nuts? Traffic not moving? Lady won't refund your gross chicken? Erickson likes to remind himself, "Hey, at least nobody is shooting at me."

> "Speaking your thoughts out loud can keep you calm and keep those around you calm."

Think Positive, Get Lucky

SERENDIPITY ISN'T ENTIRELY A MATTER OF CHANCE. IT'S MORE PREDICTABLE THAN THAT. EXPERTS HAVE IDENTIFIED FOUR HABITS THAT CAN SET US UP FOR GOOD FORTUNE

BY KATE ROCKWOOD

WHEN ANNA Z. MOVED TO CHICAGO, ONE OF THE FIRST THINGS she did was join a meet-up group for Arabic speakers. "I love trying new things," she explains. "I saw this group and thought, 'Why not?' " As luck would have it, the organizer was born and raised in Fez, Morocco, the city where Anna lived when she was learning the language. The two struck up a conversation, and today they're happily married with a little boy.

Some people might say that kismet led Anna to her future husband within a week of landing in a new city. But Anna's openness to life's quirky possibilities put her in the right place at the right time to create her own fate.

Contrary to what most of us believe, luck isn't some mysterious force. "There are huge chance factors that affect what happens to us, of course," says Richard Wiseman, a psychology professor at the University of Hertfordshire in England and author of *The Luck Factor*. "But to a very large extent, we are responsible for much of the good fortune that we encounter." And some folks tend to be naturally skilled at spotting good fortune around every turn. To learn how those "lucky" souls do it, Wiseman and other experts have been studying the traits that separate them from the rest. These four habits can help us all catch a few more breaks.

Optimists actually win more prizes, because they're willing to try again even after losing.

Expect good things

The first rule of lucky people? They feel lucky, which tilts the scales of serendipity in their favor. It has nothing to do with hocus-pocus, says Wiseman, who has spent more than 15 years researching folks' perceptions of their fate: "People who count themselves lucky expect the best outcomes, and their expectations become self-fulfilling prophecies."

Researchers at New York University discovered this effect among lovesick undergraduates. In the study, students who believed that they would get a date were significantly more likely to win over the object of their desire.

Credit self-assurance. If you believe you'll do well—whether you're trying to impress a crush or a new client—you're more motivated to persist until you succeed. Feeling lucky might even help you win the prize at a charity dinner: the more optimistic you are, the more raffle tickets you'll probably buy (and the

more likely you'll be to buy tickets next time, despite losing in the past).

Not a Pollyanna by nature? You might want to pick up a rabbit's foot—seriously. Research suggests that lucky charms work by boosting a person's confidence. In a 2010 study at the University of Cologne in Germany, superstitious subjects were asked to play a memory game; people who got to keep their talismans nearby while they played scored higher than those who played without them.

The researchers observed the same phenomenon among golfers told that they were playing with a lucky ball: the belief that they had an edge led them to putt better than golfers in a control group.

Donald Saucier, an associate professor of psychology at Kansas State University, encourages using (harmless) good-luck rituals: "These optimistic gestures are good at creating comfort—and that can help you perform better."

Court chance

Good fortune finds certain people because they make themselves easy to find, says Tania Luna, co-author of *Surprise: Embrace the Unpredictable and Engineer the Unexpected*. "Lucky people court chance by breaking routine, saying yes more often and meeting people beyond their circle," she notes.

Indeed, Wiseman has learned that the fortunate cultivate lots of friends and acquaintances. In one study, he showed people a list of common last names and asked them to indicate if they were on a first-name basis with at least one person who had each surname. Nearly 50% of people who considered themselves lucky ticked eight names or more. Only 25% of the "unlucky" could do the same.

"Lucky people talk to lots of people, attract people to them and keep in touch," Wiseman says. "These habits result in a 'network of luck,' creating potential for fortuitous connections."

Look for silver linings

Even if something doesn't turn out the way you wanted, consider that it may be a blessing in disguise. "When you reframe a situation in your mind, your brain actually processes it differently," Luna explains. For a study published in the *Journal of Child Psychology and Psychiatry*, she showed kids intense images—like a dog growling—while measuring their brain activity. Then she had them look at the images again and offered reassuring explanations, like "This dog is defending a little girl." Their brains exhibited a dramatic drop in activity in the amygdala—the region that processes fear. "It was like they were seeing completely different photos," she says.

The lucky reframe negative experiences in a similar way, Wiseman says, which helps them to continue taking chances. To get past setbacks, Luna advises asking yourself: What is one bright side effect? What have I learned? What do I want now? And how can

I get it? "Lucky people know that with uncertainty comes opportunity," she says. "Fortunately for everyone else, shifting how you perceive things is a trainable skill."

Trust your gut

Elizabeth B. remembers her luckiest moment well: She was driving home to New York from her parents' house in Pennsylvania a few years ago when something told her to stop and buy a lottery ticket. "I never, ever play the lottery," she says, "but the idea popped into my head and I listened." After she pulled over, a terrible accident occurred just ahead on the road: "A pickup had crossed into my lane and crashed into a guardrail. If I hadn't stopped, my car would have been totaled."

Maybe Elizabeth's pit stop was a fortuitous fluke. Or maybe her intuition had warned her to get away from an erratic driver approaching in the distance. She can't be sure. But what scientists do know is that we process far more visual information and other sensory details than we consciously realize, which sometimes leads to instincts we can't explain.

> *We process far more visual information and other sensory details than we consciously realize.*

Intuitive feelings hit you on a visceral level before your consciousness catches up. A study by the U.K.'s Medical Research Council demonstrated this effect. Researcher Barnaby Dunn asked people to turn over cards from four decks while he monitored their heart rates. What they didn't know was that the game was rigged: two of the decks were stacked with high-value cards, and two with bad cards. After just a few rounds, the players' heart rates dipped when they went near the high-value decks, indicating that their bodies had detected the difference in the decks before their minds figured it out.

A gut check may improve your luck in another way, too, Starr says: "It can help you act more decisively." A hunch about your fate may be just the bump in confidence you need to reach for the stars—and make them align.

PART THREE

Free Your Feelings

"The deeper that sorrow carves into your being, the more joy you can contain."

—KAHLIL GIBRAN,
"ON JOY AND SORROW"

Life After Death

WHEN SHE LOST HER HUSBAND,
FACEBOOK'S SHERYL SANDBERG ALSO
LOST HER BEARINGS. NOW SHE WANTS TO
HELP OTHERS FIND A WAY THROUGH GRIEF

BY BELINDA LUSCOMBE

FOR DAVE GOLDBERG, MAY 1, 2015, WAS THE BEST DAY WITH THE worst ending. The SurveyMonkey CEO was celebrating the 50th birthday of one of his closest buddies at a palm-fringed, $12,750-a-night villa in Punta Mita, a secluded Mexican resort favored by the Silicon Valley elite. The vacation had been full of what he loved: games with family and friends, walks and long talks by the pool. When he climbed on the fitness-center tread-mill that Friday, nothing but blue sky appeared ahead: his company was doing well, his children were healthy, and he was as in love as ever with his superwoman wife, Sheryl Sandberg, Face-book's COO and the author of *Lean In*. Then his heart gave out.

Goldberg—Goldie to his friends—was only 47 when his younger brother Rob, Rob's wife and Sandberg found him lying in a halo of blood, his skin blue. "I started doing CPR," says Rob. "I remember not being sure if I could feel a pulse or if it was really my own heart pounding." Goldberg was rushed to San Javier Hospital, a dimly lit medical center. Sandberg and one of her best friends, Marne Levine, sat on the linoleum floor waiting for a doctor to give them the news they didn't want.

In short order—though she says it felt agonizingly slow—Sandberg, the complex-problem solver, the micromanager, the

Sandberg, at home, wears her wedding ring on her right hand and Dave's ring as a pendant.

person with an almost freakish understanding of how to arrive at the best possible results, was thrust against something unfamiliar: an outcome she couldn't change. "The wails of her crying in that hospital were unlike anything that I'd ever heard in my life," says Phil Deutch, Levine's husband and the person whose birthday they were celebrating. "It was an awful, awful scene."

As they were leaving Goldberg's body for the last time, Sandberg ran back to give him one more hug. "I think for Sheryl, letting go of him physically meant letting go of the moment that this could somehow not be real," says Rob. "I had to gently pull her off of him. She just wanted to hug him and wanted him to be there and wanted him to come back."

Dying is not a technical glitch of the human operating system; it's a feature. It's the only prediction we can make at birth that we can bank on. Everyone will die, and it's very likely somebody we love will die before we do. And yet the bereaved are often treated like those to whom something unnatural or disgraceful has happened. People avoid them, don't invite them out, fall silent when they enter the room. The grieving are often isolated when they most need community.

That's a problem that Sandberg, now 48, can work with. The woman who urged the world to lean in has undertaken a campaign to help people push on, to bounce back from horrible misfortune. Her newest book, *Option B: Facing Adversity, Building Resilience, and Finding Joy*, is a primer for those who are bereaved, to help them recover and find happiness. But it's also a guide for the unscathed on how to help people "lean in to the suck," as Sandberg's rabbi puts it.

She wrote the book with her friend and collaborator Adam Grant, a psychologist and the author of the best sellers *Originals* and *Give and Take*. Like *Lean In*, *Option B* comes with a nonprofit launched by the Sheryl Sandberg & Dave Goldberg Family Foundation. The or-

> ## The bereaved are often treated like those to whom something unnatural or disgraceful has happened.

ganization aims to "change the conversation around adversity," Sandberg's representatives say. If that seems vague, recall that nobody really knew what the Lean In Circles were supposed to do either—but there are now 30,000 of them in 150 countries.

Some might argue that Sandberg is the wrong teacher for a course in hard knocks. After all, her life, from the outside, seems a mind-bogglingly privileged existence among brainiac titans. She's a billionaire in no danger of losing her job, no matter how much time she takes off. She can afford round-the-clock therapy, and her network can put her in touch with anyone.

Sandberg is well aware of her advantages. (And in case she needed a reminder, author Camille Paglia called her "insufferably smug and entitled.") But she has deployed a disadvantage as her ultimate asset: vulnerability. In June 2015, a month into her widowhood, after a particularly lousy day, Sandberg posted on Facebook the social-media equivalent of Edvard Munch's *Scream*. "I think when tragedy occurs, it presents a choice," she wrote. "You can give in to the void, the emptiness that fills your heart, your lungs, constricts your ability to think or even breathe. Or you can try to find meaning. These past 30 days, I have spent many of my moments lost in that void." Suddenly, Superwoman became very human.

Except because she is the kind of person who always has at hand a Ziploc bag filled with exactly the right number of macadamia nuts, Sandberg's howl into the void came with helpful tips. Don't avoid the heartbroken (except when they obviously want to be avoided). Don't tell them that everything will be OK, because, well, how would you know? And don't ask the bereaved how they are. Instead, ask them how they are that day.

None of the advice in the post or in the book is particularly new. Grief is not a novel problem. But not very many folks with Sandberg's platform and pain have talked about it,

Sheryl and Dave on their wedding day, Apr. 17, 2004, in Carefree, Ariz.

with the intent of starting a movement. "She was able to find some gratitude," says Grant, "and really think about how she could share the experience she had in a way that would help other people."

Sandberg's 2015 post soon drew tens of thousands of comments, including ones from Facebook employees who didn't know how to react to their famous boss, who occasionally broke down in tears in a meeting—which, as Sandberg writes, is not the kind of disruption Silicon Valley is looking for.

"I think a lot of people wanted to reach out to her, but they didn't know how," says Facebook CEO Mark Zuckerberg. "You know, there's this whole question of, Are you reopening a wound or something? And of course, what she would say is 'You're not reopening the wound. I mean, it's, like, open and gaping.'"

A month before Goldberg died, Tracy Zamot, a music publicist in New York, also lost her husband suddenly, of a pulmonary embolism. She says Sandberg's post had a real effect on the way people talked to her. "The minute she wrote, 'How are you today?' people started asking me that," she says, which made answering the question much easier. "I didn't feel like I was going to explode into a ball of flames every time I had to answer."

Sandberg claims that she shared her feelings on impulse, but the response pushed her to action. "I got so much of this wrong, so much of this wrong," she says in her glass-walled conference room, which is identified by a small plaque near the door that reads ONLY GOOD NEWS.

To Grant, a Wharton School professor, Sandberg has made a contribution not just

In the wake of Sandberg's loss, she and Zuckerberg changed Facebook's leave policies.

to self-help but also to leadership. "I would like more leaders to realize what Sheryl did through living it," he says. "Expressing emotion when you've gone through extreme pain is not weakness. It is humanity."

In the weeks after Goldberg died, even before she posted on Facebook, Sandberg had been codifying her agony in a journal and sharing it with a few close confidantes. "I wrote and I wrote and I wrote," she says. Keeping a journal is one of the activities she recommends to ease the grieving process. "Literally all I did was my kids, come to work and write." The 100,000-plus words she eventually wrote were a big part of her recovery and became the spine of her book.

What Sandberg learned, with the help of Grant, was that there are three myths people cling to that make it harder to spring back from adversity. The first is that they're somehow responsible for what happened to them. The second is that sadness must carpet their lives from wall to wall. And the third is that they will never feel any better. Ever the communicator, Sandberg invokes what psychologists who study helplessness refer to as the three p's: thinking about adversity as personal, pervasive and permanent.

The lessons, which she says she wishes she knew when her first marriage ended in divorce, didn't come easily. Grant told Sandberg she had to ban the word "sorry." "Sheryl likes to ban things that are not productive, like #banbossy," he says, citing Sandberg's campaign to stop using a word about girls that is never used to describe boys. "There's no more effective way to argue with someone who's strong-willed than to turn their own words around on them."

Her tendency to apologize was the result of an unexpected symptom of her grief: Sandberg completely lost her self-confidence. "It just kind of crumbled in every area," she says. "I didn't think I could be a good friend. I didn't feel like I could do my job." She wasn't even sure she could look after her grieving kids. This surprised Sandberg as much as anyone: "It reminded me of how one day in my neighborhood I watched a house that had taken years to build get torn down in a matter of minutes," she writes in *Option B*. "Boom. Flattened."

On her first day back at work, she says, she fell asleep in a meeting, rambled and misidentified a colleague, then left at 2 p.m. to pick up her kids from school. That evening she called Zuckerberg to see if she should even be there. "Mark said, 'Take the time off you need,' " says Sandberg. "And that's what I would have said to someone in the same situation. But then he said, 'Actually I'm really glad you were here today. You made two really good points—here's what they were.' "

That small vote of confidence led to one of the biggest changes Sandberg made in her management style: she no longer automatically diverts work from people facing personal adversity. Now she asks if they want to do it because, counterintuitively, re-

Don't ask the bereaved how they are. Instead ask them how they are that day.

lieving people of some of their responsibilities could mean denying them a way of finding their bearings.

When Caryn Marooney was diagnosed with breast cancer shortly after she was asked to head up global communications at Facebook, Sandberg encouraged her to take the promotion. "Sheryl had been a vulnerable leader that I had gotten to see close-up," says Marooney. She took the job, and in one of her first meetings with her team members she let them know she was undergoing treatment. "It helped people share things with me in a way that helped me understand how to do the job better and faster," Marooney says.

Silicon Valley wasn't all so gentle and touchy-feely. Another friend, venture capitalist Chamath Palihapitiya, told Sandberg to remember her ambition and "get back on the motherf---ing path." He also gave her a chain to wear Goldberg's wedding band around her neck. (Zuckerberg had also given her a chain, so Sandberg—half empath, half Spock—had them welded together at the ends and wears both.)

Over time, Sandberg began to emerge from the fog. Her mom didn't have to lie beside her every night as she cried herself to sleep. She danced at a party and felt momentarily happy. She didn't travel as much or have as many work dinners, but she got out. She started playing the piano again after 30 years and created new rituals with her kids: they started biking and having weekly "family awesome fun," in which one child chooses an activity. She also lets the kids have sleepovers, which Goldberg, who thought his kids, now 9 and 12, needed sleep, had not allowed.

Encouraged by her in-laws, Sandberg eventually started dating, too. Her current beau is Bobby Kotick, who runs the gaming company Activision Blizzard and comes from the same brand of cuddly mensch as Goldberg. She has replaced the photo of a beach at dusk in her bedroom with one of a beach during the day. She's even taken back birthdays. First she started celebrating her own, which she used to do only every five years.

"She embraces joy in a different way than she has before," says friend Levine. "She tries to make her birthdays as joyful as possible." On Goldberg's birthday, the kids play poker, his favorite game, in which they are being coached by Palihapitiya, who has competed in the World Series of Poker championships.

She even had a party for Deutch, whose birthday will forever be associated with Goldberg's death. "You know, it's never going to be the same," Deutch says, "but she really went to great efforts to help take a day that's pretty dark and change it."

Sandberg, too, is changed. "I think she just has more perspective," says Zuckerberg. When he first got the message from her on that Friday night that said "Urgent, please call," he thought it was probably a work issue, even though she was on vacation. "A lot of things used to be 'Urgent, please call,'" he says. "These days they're not. But I think that that's made her a better leader." For her part, Sandberg says, "Mark's one of the people who really carried me. I believe even more I work with the greatest person in the world."

Sandberg has faced adversity, developed resilience and found some joy. But what she can't do anything about—what still makes her lower the remote-controlled blinds in her meeting room at work and weep every time she talks about it—is the fact that she cannot give her kids their father back.

Telling them he was gone was the hardest thing she has ever done. She avoids talking about it, but in *Option B* she writes that "nothing has come close to the pain of this moment. Even now when my mind wanders back, I shake and my throat constricts."

The difficulties of being a single mother, even a highly resourced one, came as a shock to Sandberg. They made her rethink some of *Lean In*. "When I look back at the chapter called 'Make Your Partner a Real Partner,' it has, like, a big old assumption that you have a

> *The difficulties of being a single mother, even a highly resourced one, came as a shock.*

partner," she says. "I got that wrong."

Almost 10 million women are single mothers in the U.S., and about one third of those households live in poverty—something that enrages Sandberg. "I think it's part of why I have become so outspoken on public policy now," she says. "I'm in a different place."

On Father's Day, she and her children went to a camp for kids whose dads are incarcerated. And in April, she promoted a campaign to draw attention to the gender pay gap by persuading businesses to charge 20% less for a day.

She wants to see changes in maternity leave, paternity leave and living-wage laws. But she's even less inclined than she was before Goldberg died to enter public office—partly because her focus is on her kids and partly because she feels she can move the needle more effectively from where she is. "My loyalty to Mark was deep before and is deeper now," she says. Facebook implemented a slew of new bereavement and family-illness leave policies, which she hopes will pressure other tech companies to follow suit.

But the more mundane stuff breaks her heart too. "Does there have to be a father-daughter dance?" she asks. "My kids will say things like 'You're the only parent I have left.' Or my daughter has been talking about how she doesn't remember her father, his voice. She said, 'I'm glad I have video, because I didn't think his voice sounded like that.'" The remote-controlled blinds come down. "I feel it every day. Every day. I go to my son's basketball game, and there are a lot of fathers there. My daughter is going to be in the school play next week, and Dave is not here to go to any of that."

A few weeks after Goldberg died, there was a father-child event at the kids' school, and Deutch proposed designating a stand-in dad. Sandberg protested that it wasn't the same as having Goldberg there. Deutch put his arm around her. "Option A is not available," he said. "So let's just kick the s--- out of Option B."

"DAVE WAS A ROCK. DAVE WAS MY ROCK."

Goldberg was smitten with Sandberg from the first movie they saw together—*Courage Under Fire*—but it took Sandberg six years to come around. Their 11th wedding anniversary was a few weeks before he died, and Sandberg regrets spending it apart. "Dave was one of the most humble, grounded, confident people I've ever met," says his friend Phil Deutch (pictured in group photo, middle left). "They were fun and great to be around, and interested and curious, as people, as a couple. They really navigated life." Goldberg advised Sandberg to join Facebook, and he warned her that the first draft of *Lean In* was "like eating your Wheaties" and needed more personal details. He was widely recognized as the Silicon Valley sage most generous with his time. "I realize how biased I am, but I think the world lost something incredibly special when they lost Dave," says Sandberg. "I meet people on a weekly basis who tell me, 'Dave changed my life.' "

Healthy Ways to Get Angry

IF YOU'RE FUMING AND NOT DOING MUCH ABOUT IT, YOU'RE NOT ALONE. BUT STIFLING FURY MAY MAKE THINGS WORSE. HERE'S HOW TO MANAGE THIS TRICKY EMOTION AND GET TO A CALMER STATE

BY CARA BIRNBAUM

WHEN YOU HEAR THE WORDS "ANGER PROBLEM," YOU DON'T think of someone like Bethany. Actually, the 40-something sales analyst and mother of one in Brooklyn, N.Y., says she rarely gets full-throttle angry. Instead, she'll spend weeks stewing over a self-entitled co-worker or her own hatred of the gym. Nobody would know, though; she keeps it all to herself.

Which is exactly the problem. The danger isn't feeling anger—an emotion hardwired into the human brain—but burying that useful response until it turns into a quiet simmering. Women, in particular, may have been raised to not make a scene. We are often overworked, sleep-deprived, always on call and generally cranky about it. And as anyone with a social-media account knows, we feel outraged daily—about GMOs, the future of the planet, the Kardashians, you name it. In fact, "the modern, connected lifestyle has put us in an almost constant state of tension," says Ryan Martin, chair of the psychology department at the University of Wisconsin–Green Bay and founder of the blog All the Rage.

Although you don't want to explode, holding in the emotion could be just as bad for you. "Rumination is like a ticking time bomb," says Matthew Zawadzki, an assistant professor of health psychology at the University of California, Merced. A paper he

co-authored suggested that simply thinking about whatever pissed you off days, weeks or even months earlier jacks up your blood pressure and heart rate as much as the original event did.

Whether you stew or rage, your anger is trying to tell you something—about your life, mind and body. Here's how to use it as a catalyst for change.

Adrenaline rush

As bad as being peeved feels, it's actually a protective response to what usually starts out as fear or pain, explains Veronica Rojas, a psychiatrist specializing in child and adolescent psychiatry. Before you can even make sense of a threat, your amygdala—the almond-shaped emotion center of the brain—triggers a release of adrenaline and other stress hormones. Your energy surges as your breathing quickens and your heart rate and blood pressure rise. "Your face might flush, your thoughts narrow, and it's very difficult to think about anything else for a few minutes," says Rojas. It takes several seconds for that initial burst of fear or pain to become anger. As you start thinking things through, your analytical prefrontal cortex—the brain's chief decision maker—contextualizes the threat: Why does she speak to me that way? How am I still working at this lousy job? "That's why we call anger a secondary emotion," explains Rojas. "It never occurs alone." It's your brain's way of jolting you out of a vulnerable place and into self-protection mode.

Most of us stop short of putting on the boxing gloves. The prefrontal cortex nips angry impulses in the bud. But if you constantly tamp down your annoyance, those blood-pumping stress hormones can remain elevated, says Rojas. Research from Carnegie Mellon University in 2012 found that prolonged psychological stress leaves you more prone to a host of illnesses and diseases, partly by interfering with your immune system's ability to regulate inflammation throughout the body.

Anger is your brain's way of jolting you out of a vulnerable place and into self-protection mode.

Damage control

Short-term simmering all too often becomes chronic: the higher your stress level, the more an otherwise minor issue (like someone swiping your skinny latte) makes you ready to burst into flames. Snapping—whether it's at that coffee thief at Starbucks or that fake-news-spreading friend on social media—can worsen matters. "Anger is the most viral emotion," says Martin. It's more contagious than joy and sadness, according to a 2013 study that looked at social networks.

Brooding over your feelings may be no better: researchers have long established that rumination contributes to depression and anxiety. When Rojas sees patients suffering from either of the above, it often turns out to be rooted in years of anger.

The same can be true for high blood pressure, irritable bowel syndrome, headaches and a host of other chronic ailments, all of which can be exacerbated by persistently high levels of stress hormones, says Mary Coussons-Read, a professor of psychology at the University of Colorado at Colorado Springs. And, tellingly, married couples who regularly suppress anger have a higher risk of premature death than those who express it, according to University of Michigan research.

Of course, the news isn't great for folks who repeatedly lash out, either. Research in the *European Heart Journal* showed that the risk of heart attack is nearly five times as high in the two hours after an angry outburst.

How to get mad

So what's a ticked-off person to do? Remember that anger is a flashing sign telling you to address something. "Conflict is healthy only if you try to figure out what's wrong and do something about it," says Ernest Harburg, a research scientist emeritus in epidemiology and psychology at the University of Michigan. First, though, take a moment to note the reaction: "If anger arises, observe your bodily sensations without trying to push

Rage-Proof Your Days

The prickly, stressed-out state we're often in before an angry stimulus hits—what psychologists call "pre-anger"—is important to manage to avoid full-on rage. These little steps will help keep insignificant triggers from getting you worked up

UNFRIEND AS NEEDED

Hide posts from those social-media Negative Nellies forever posting terrible news you have no power to change. Get them off your feed for a month and see if you miss waking up to the angst.

DON'T GET HANGRY

A healthy carb with fiber, combined with a little protein—like an apple and a cup of yogurt, or whole-wheat crackers with peanut butter—will help keep blood sugar and mood on an even keel.

DECLUTTER YOUR DESK

No one is saying you have to go all Marie Kondo and eliminate all belongings that don't bring you joy, but "many people feel calmer and more in control when their work and living spaces are tidy," says happiness expert Gretchen Rubin.

DO ONE THING AT A TIME

Studies show that multitasking makes us sloppy and less efficient. And as psychologist Ryan Martin points out, it pretty much ensures you'll feel constantly interrupted and snippy about it.

them away," advises Susan Smalley, a professor emeritus of psychiatry and founder of the Mindful Awareness Research Center at UCLA. Relax your shoulders and breathe deeply so your stomach slowly rises and falls—all cues to the mind that your body is calming down.

Leave the scene if you can, adds Gail Saltz, a clinical associate professor of psychiatry at Weill Cornell Medical College: "It's OK to say, 'I notice myself feeling pretty tapped out. I want to be able to discuss this logically, so I'm going to take a walk.'" Even ducking into the bathroom gives you a few minutes to reset. For Rojas, running a stream of water over one wrist does the trick. For Coussons-Read, it's singing "Viva Las Vegas" in her head.

With calm should come the clarity needed to problem-solve, says Gretchen Rubin, the best-selling author of *The Happiness Project* and *Better Than Before*. "If you feel angry going to work every day," she asks, "is it because work seems meaningless? Because you can never get all your tasks done? Or because you have a conflict with a co-worker?" They're all legit reasons—each with its own path to resolution.

Asking yourself questions like these may loosen anger's grip, letting you see events in context. "A common setup for anger is not thinking about what the other person is going through," says Alice Domar, the executive director of the Domar Center for Mind/Body Health in Boston. When you do so, you can get to constructive dialogue, which allows you to avoid the feeling of powerlessness that can cause anxiety and depression. It's all about taking action—only not in anger this time.

Instagram Envy, Tamed

DO FRIENDS' SOCIAL-MEDIA POSTS SOUND MORE LIKE BRAGS THAN UPDATES? HAD IT WITH THEIR PARADISE VACATION PHOTOS? THIS IS HOW ONE WOMAN FOUND (A LITTLE) PERSPECTIVE

BY JANCEE DUNN

THE OTHER DAY, I WAS SO PLEASED WITH AN APRICOT-ALMOND smoothie I made that I decided to post a picture of it on Instagram. First, though, I browsed friends' feeds. Forty-five minutes later, I was dizzy from the endless slide show of the Perfect Life: one person serenely paddleboarding ("Got the hang of it after one lesson!"), another lounging on a hotel bed ("Just had the best. Massage. Ever"). Oh, and a smoothie—this one perched on a hibiscus-covered balcony overlooking a Caribbean beach. I grabbed my phone and deleted the photo of my now schlumpy drink.

These days, it's gotten impossible to not feel like you're being one-upped online. You ran a 5K? Big deal, when your co-worker posts pictures of her half-marathon . . . for charity. Meanwhile, social-media users have perfected the art of simultaneously moaning and boasting, a.k.a. moasting: "Someone just asked me what I was studying in college—hello, I'm 34!"

I realize these posts and pretty pictures are often curated and edited. So why do I still have that constant, dispiriting feeling that my own life pales in comparison? In fact, researchers are discovering that being immersed in everyone else's general awesomeness online can be mentally bad for you. A study from the University of Michigan showed that the more time we browse

Facebook, the more our sense of well-being and life satisfaction drop. One German study reported that after people spent time on Facebook, more than one third felt frustrated, upset or envious. (Friends' vacation snaps riled them up the most.)

This feeling is intensified as we increasingly take our relationships online, says psychologist Gregory Jantz, author of *Hooked: The Pitfalls of Media, Technology, and Social Networking*. "One of the biggest groups of Facebook users is women age 32 to 45," he notes, "and about 35% of the younger ones admit that the first thing they do after they crawl out of bed, before they go to the bathroom, is check Facebook." Adding to our neediness is the addictive—and sometimes maniacal—pursuit of "likes." According to one consumer-trends survey, 62% of people say they feel better about themselves when others approve of something they post on social media. The flip side is the insecurity that creeps in when only a few people "like" your photo, and the jealousy you feel when a friend's photo gets a flurry of thumbs-ups.

Of course, it's human nature to want to present your best self to the world. The ancient Egyptians threw on kohl liner and their most stylish linen tunic before hitting the market. "There's something alluring about creating an online persona that says, 'I'm interesting, I have a well-kept home, I eat good food—this is my life!' " says Andrea Bonior, an adjunct professor of psychology at Georgetown University. "We look to our social-media profiles to validate what we want to believe about ourselves." Yet this fluff fest can lead to anxiety about being exposed as a fraud, as in living in fear that a high school pal will comment, "I remember when you had a much larger nose!" beneath your glam shot.

To end the jolts of jealousy, Jantz has a suggestion: When you read a post that leaves you feeling less than ideal, remember that

> *We look to our social-media profiles to validate what we want to believe about ourselves.*

we all scrupulously control our self-image. I know it's true. Recently I posted a picture of myself and someone commented, "You look amazing!" Well, yes; that's because I held the camera so high above my head, it could have been a satellite photo from space. (Whereas if I look down at my phone, my reflection bears a startling likeness to Donald Trump.)

It also helps to be aware of what sets off self-doubt. "If you hate your old kitchen, maybe you shouldn't repeatedly check out Mary's kitchen renovation," Bonior says. My downfall is others' fitness triumphs. A few shots of a friend's cyclo-cross race are inspiring; scrolling through hundreds makes me think, Why bother? and shuffle off to the couch. Timing is another trigger. I look at these fabulous pics before bed, when I'm tired and need to decompress—exactly when I feel the most sensitive.

Another cyber-solution is to fully get behind your own posts. As Bonior says, "You can choose to use others' experiences as a yardstick, or you can believe your standards are valid in and of themselves." Also, remember to back away from the computer. "Relationships are best conducted in real life," Jantz says, "not 140-character sound bites."

Jantz's words were on my mind when I saw a friend's posts from a trip to Greece. Instead of caving in to jealousy, I called and told her that her photos were like a Ralph Lauren ad. She laughed and said, "Don't look too close or you'll see that my eyes are red." Ten minutes beforehand, she and her husband had had a big money fight; the trip, she conceded, was great but had been a costly mistake. We commiserated about finances and made plans to meet. I felt a surge of pleasure as I hung up.

Now if insecurity sneaks up on me while I'm online, I take it as a sign to switch gears and go for a run, make another unphotogenic smoothie or check out the YouTube clip my mother sent of, say, a Speedo-clad squirrel eating an ice cream cone. Also, maybe I'll avoid Beyoncé's Instagram account altogether.

LET GO OF GUILT

ARE YOU TOO HARD ON YOURSELF? LEARN TO CUT YOURSELF MORE SLACK WITH THIS SELF-KINDNESS PLAN

BY JACQUELINE ANDRIAKOS

The trouble with guilt:
Constantly feeling guilty gnaws at your emotional well-being and causes negativity to snowball. "It can make you feel defeated, anxious or even depressed," says Susan Krauss Whitbourne, a professor of psychological and brain sciences at the University of Massachusetts–Amherst. And we often beat ourselves up for no good reason, she adds: "Most of the time, we manufacture guilt in our minds simply because of the ridiculous expectations we set for ourselves." Lift yourself out of the spiral with this action plan.

WEEK 1: IDENTIFY YOUR GUILT TRIGGERS
"If you can learn to pause and recognize when you feel guilt coming on, you're halfway toward fixing the problem," says Whitbourne. So right off the bat, get to the bottom of what makes you feel the most remorse.

Pay attention
Notice any moments you feel guilty, as well as what prompted the pangs (you missed a deadline; you spent a lot of money). It may help to take some notes, either on paper or in your smartphone.

Look for themes
Did you get ticked at yourself each time you bought a $15 lunch this week? Do you lie in bed night after night wishing you had been more patient with your kids? Track how often specific subjects bring on regret.

Group the majors and minors
At the end of the week, pinpoint the big issues that incited guilt more than once or weighed on you more heavily than others. (You'll deal with the lesser regrets in week three.)

WEEK 2: CHANGE YOUR PERSPECTIVE
"You don't want to try to just be 'over' a guilt that's coming up a lot for you," says Whitbourne. "Pull it out, look at it, and come up with some alternative interpretations."

Envision a redo
Think (or even talk aloud) about what you wish you were doing differently— maybe you want to have a better attitude at work, or

you think you should reel in your spending by creating a budget. "It doesn't mean you have to go out and make some drastic change right this minute, but you're talking about it, and that's productive," says Susie Moore, a life coach in New York and the author of *What If It Does Work Out?*

Pick a different emotion
"Guilt and sadness and anxiety are all on a continuum in a way," says Whitbourne. "And when we're stressed, it's easy to be self-critical." Try asking, "Wait, does it really make sense to be feeling guilty at this moment? Or am I letting stress get to me?"

Realize you're human
"Perfectionism is often what drives guilt," says

Whitbourne. "At some point, you have to just accept your limitations." Moore adds that it can help to tell yourself that no parent or employee is doing everything flawlessly.

WEEK 3: SHAKE OFF THE SMALL STUFF
"To say you will never feel guilty again about something silly would be ridiculous," says Whitbourne. "But it's important to recognize when you may be blowing things out of proportion." Practice short-circuiting your regret when it's truly unnecessary.

Reframe a fail
Look at it with a practical eye. Instead of "I shouldn't have left the office early today with my current workload," tell yourself, "I needed to cut out in order to attend this doctor's appointment that was long overdue."

Laugh it off
"Humor is one of the greatest antidotes to guilt," says Whitbourne. Poke fun at yourself: You ran out of time to bake and brought a store-bought dessert to the holiday party? How dare you even show up!

Find a silver lining
Let's say you're upset with yourself because you slapped together your gift wrapping this year. "Well, you also didn't go to the department store and have them wrap it for you," says Whitbourne. "You're showing the person that you love them enough to put in the effort." Nice work.

Finding Calm in a Stressful World

A FAMILY OF WORRYWARTS HELPS EACH OTHER COPE WITH THE UNKNOWN

BY KRISTIN VAN OGTROP

MY YOUNGEST SON, WHO IS 10, HAS LONG HAD AN OBSESSION THAT crops up whenever we get in the car. As he climbs into the back seat, he will peer over my shoulder at the dashboard and, depending on his mood, may ask the question we both know he is thinking: "Are we going to run out of gas?"

My youngest sister—his aunt—is a therapist and the wise woman who taught me the possible-probable trick. And so I say to my son: "Is it possible for our Subaru to run out of gas when it has half a tank and we are only driving two miles to Costco and back? Perhaps. But it is definitely not probable."

Possible versus probable. When applied in the right circumstance, it almost always gives you the right answer. Even better, it gives you the feeling that you are in control.

For the record, we have never run out of gas. And I would rather not take this particular, seemingly nonsensical gas-tank worry seriously. But given our gene pool, I know I should. My son hails from a long line of people who used to be called worrywarts—ask me sometime about my childhood fear of vomiting—until the 21st century arrived and we woke up one day to learn that we actually suffer from anxiety, in varying degrees. (If you were to meet my child, you would find a happy, charming, intellectually curious fellow. But

Some people are drawn to new adventures and experiences, while other people shy away from them.

you're not driving to Costco with him.) Anxiety has impacted the lives of several of my family members in serious ways that I am not permitted, per unspoken family law, to discuss here. And we are far from alone. More than 6 million American teens will develop an anxiety disorder, according to National Institute of Mental Health data; at my son's most recent checkup, his pediatrician remarked matter-of-factly that treatment solutions haven't kept pace with the number of anxious kids.

Which brings me to the strong control-freak current also running through our gene pool. Supposedly, controlling parents are more likely to produce anxious children. But there is a fine line between setting boundaries and controlling, between guiding choices and telling your kids what to do because Mom actually does know best a good deal of the time. At age 10, my son has reached a childhood inflection point, approaching the end of elementary school, crossing over from the years when I had control over much of his existence to the years when it becomes increasingly clear how little control I really have.

When your son is 10, his worries seem quaint: little kids, little problems. But his two older brothers, who are 19 and 22, are big kids now, with their big-kid problems stretching into their youngest sibling's understanding of the world the way their long legs stretch clear under the kitchen table at dinner. When we sit as a family at that table, the older boys are protective of their young brother and his innocence: they know not to curse, not to listen to songs with

vulgar lyrics, not to talk about friends who drink too much or smoke weed or skip class. Still, things happen in the lives of 19- and 22-year-olds that demand dinner-table discussion. And so, as the little guy listens, wide-eyed and silent, scary stories unfold: from the inconvenient (a minor car accident) to the truly heartbreaking (a roommate whose life ended before he could graduate from college). Is this why, when I recently took his eldest brother to the emergency room for what turned out to be a stomach virus, my youngest asked, "Is he going to die?"

Possible versus probable is not foolproof. My two older sons have reached an age at which it doesn't work on them. They are old enough to have learned that tragically improbable things do happen, that parents can't control much and that helpful constructs from Aunt Claire won't erase a biological inheritance generations in the making. As they have grown into young men, I have become less a boundary setter. Less a guide. More a . . . presence. A loving, nonjudgmental (well, I try) and constant presence.

And with my sweet, wide-eyed 10-year-old who alternately seems to understand nothing at all and far too much, I will cling to possible versus probable for as long as it works. Perhaps the very things I do to try to protect him just make him more vulnerable to anxiety. Smarter minds than I will have to figure that one out. But I know one thing for certain, which is that my wonderful little boy has all the time in the world to learn how sad and uncertain life can be. And once he does, there will be only so much I can do.

HOW TO HAVE AN AWESOME LIFE

YOU DON'T HAVE TO BE 18 TO FEEL BLOWN AWAY BY THE WONDER OF IT ALL. CULTIVATE THE FEEL-GOOD EMOTION OF AWE AT ANY AGE

BY LISA LOMBARDI

When was the last time you went: *Whoa?*

If it was a trip to the Grand Canyon three summers ago, it may be time to wake up your sense of wonder. A growing body of research is showing that awe—that feeling of astonishment when in the presence of something vast and hard to comprehend—bolsters our health, emotional well-being and connection to the world.

It also leads to greater humility, according to new research out of the University of California, Berkeley's Social Interaction Lab. "Many people are concerned about the rise of narcissism, arrogance and greed," says lead researcher Dacher Keltner, a professor of psychology at U.C. Berkeley and the faculty director of its Greater Good Science Center. "One antidote is humility: the clear-eyed view of the self, sense of strength in others and realization that you are part of something larger."

WHERE DOES AWE COME FROM?

"In studies across 28 cultures, we've found the two main sources of awe are other people and nature," says Keltner. We are awed not only by genius but also by kindness. A woman giving birth may trigger this emotion; so can children playing. Religious rituals and great music, art and architecture may also give you goose bumps (a physiological result of awe).

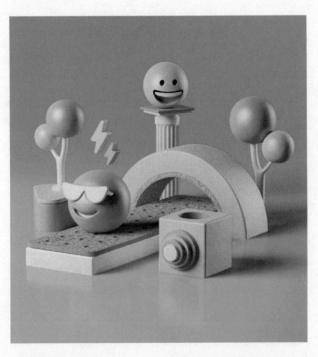

"We've been struck by how much awe there is in everyday life," reports Keltner, who is also the author of *The Power Paradox: How We Gain and Lose Influence*. "On average, people are feeling awe 2.5 times a week, from many sources—patterns of light, the sound of rain, clouds, the generosity of others, cool graffiti."

HOW IT HELPS US

Being in the presence of something transcendent makes us feel less important—in a good way. "When we are in Yosemite, we draw ourselves as smaller," Keltner says. "In our awe research, people describe feeling small—'I feel like a tiny speck in the universe.' " The upside? You see yourself as part of something bigger.

In fact, awe may actually make us nicer: In one U.C. Berkeley study, researchers had one group of people gaze up at eucalyptus trees for one minute and another group look at a nondescript building. Then the researchers stumbled and dropped pens. The people with the amazing view picked up more pens. "After walking in the woods, you come out feeling at peace with other people," Keltner says, and that makes you more likely to notice and assist others in need.

AWE'S IMMUNE BOOST

Feeling astonished may even change your body on a cellular level. Inflammation "is a major prediction of disease," Keltner says, linked to depression, autoimmune diseases and diabetes. In one study by Keltner and Jennifer Stellar, a graduate of U.C. Berkeley now at the University of Toronto, people who reported the most awe ("I'm always thinking of the mysteries of the world") had lower levels of IL6, a biomarker of inflammation.

HOW TO FEEL WONDERSTRUCK

First, we have to power down our devices. "Many people are starved for awe because they don't get outside," Keltner points out. "Screens only amplify the problem, preventing us from looking at things for an extended period."

Every day, urges Keltner, take a few minutes to try to find your daily dose of goose bumps. Stop to take in a street performer's act. Listen to a song that unites all the periods of your life. Watch birds as they land on your bird feeder and scatter.

Or really get out into nature. Keltner's last moment of awe was, well, awesome: "I was just camping by myself in the Sierras and reading a book about the origins of religious thought, when I looked up and saw a bear about four feet away, looking right into my eyes."

Joy

A FEELING IN PHOTOS

TOGETHERNESS

Schoolchildren celebrating
Independence Day in
the northern Indian
city of Chandigarh,
Aug. 15, 2009

OUT OF THIS WORLD

On Aug. 5, 2012, NASA's
Mars Science Laboratory
Team rejoiced after learning
the Curiosity rover had
landed safely on Mars.

After returning from a seven-month tour in Iraq on Sept. 11, 2007, Terri Gurrola reunited with her daughter Gabrielle, then 3.

AMERICAN TALE

Brazilian immigrant Gleidson Hoffman celebrated after becoming an American citizen during a naturalization ceremony at One World Trade Center in New York on Aug. 15, 2017.

TIME

Editor Nancy Gibbs
Creative Director D.W. Pine
Director of Photography Kira Pollack

The Science of Emotions

Editor Lisa Lombardi
Designer Skye Gurney
Photo Editor Crary Pullen
Writers Jacqueline Andriakos, Emily Barone, Cara Birnbaum, Dan Bova, Susan David, Jancee Dunn, Ginny Graves, Anne Kreamer, Belinda Luscombe, Marcia Menter, Mandy Oaklander, Leslie Pepper, Sara Reistad-Long, Kate Rockwood, Alexandra Sifferlin, Kristin Van Ogtrop, Yolanda Wikiel, Meg Wolitzer
Copy Editor Joseph McCombs
Reporter David Bjerklie
Editorial Production David Sloan

TIME INC. BOOKS
Publisher Margot Schupf
Vice President, Finance Cateryn Kiernan
Vice President, Marketing Jeremy Biloon
Executive Director, Marketing Services Carol Pittard
Director, Brand Marketing Jean Kennedy
Sales Director Christi Crowley
Associate Director, Finance Jill Earyes
Associate Director, Brand Marketing Bryan Christian
Assistant General Counsel Andrew Goldberg
Assistant Director, Production Susan Chodakiewicz
Senior Manager, Finance Ashley Petrasovic
Brand Manager Katherine Barnet
Prepress Manager Alex Voznesenskiy
Project Manager Hillary Leary

Editorial Director Kostya Kennedy
Creative Director Gary Stewart
Director of Photography Christina Lieberman
Editorial Operations Director Jamie Roth Major
Senior Editor Alyssa Smith
Manager, Editorial Operations Gina Scauzillo
Associate Art Director Allie Adams
Copy Chief Rina Bander
Assistant Editor Courtney Mifsud

Special Thanks Melissa Frankenberry, Kristina Jutzi, Simon Keeble, Seniqua Koger, Kate Roncinske, Kristen Zwicker

ABOUT THE ARTIST

The imaginative 3-D illustrations seen throughout the book were created by Barcelona-based artist Nuria Madrid. "I love colors, isometric images, geometry and detail-filled compositions," says Madrid. For this project, she collaborated with artist Cristian García to bring the complex subject of understanding emotions to life.

Credits

FRONT COVER SensorSpot/ Getty Images (4) **BACK COVER** Fstoplight/Getty Images **TITLE PAGE** Flashpop/Getty Images **CONTENTS 2–3** Henrik Sorenson/Getty Images **INTRODUCTION 5** molotovcoketail/Getty Images **PART ONE 6–7** Nuria Madrid for TIME **8** Pixelfit/Getty Images **11** Courtesy of the Yale Center for Emotional Intellligence **12** Image Source/ Getty Images **14–15** Daniel Ingold/Getty Images **16–17** Heritage Images/Getty Images **18** Klaus Vedfelt/Getty Images **21** Nuria Madrid for TIME **22** Sam Kaplan/Trunk Archive **25** Jamie Grill/Getty Images **26** Walter Hodges/Getty Images **27** Nuria Madrid for TIME **28** Upper Cut Images/ Getty Images **31** Illustration by Brown Bird Design for TIME **35** Tom Merten/Getty Images **36** (clockwise from left) Mauren Caruso/Getty Images; s-cphoto/Getty Images; design 56/Getty Images **37** (from left) rimglow/Getty Images; Yasin Guneysu/Getty Images **PART TWO 38–39** Nuria Madrid for TIME **40** Christine Glade/Getty Images **43** Antonio Guillem/ Getty Images **44** Lucia Lambrex/Getty Images **46–47** Shutterstock **49** Prado, Madrid, Spain/Bridgeman Images **50–51** Bartek Szewczyk/Getty Images **52** Ryan McVay/Getty Images (hallway); Deborah Harrison/ Getty Images (balloon) **55** Michael Jung/Getty Images **56** Vadym Drobot/Alamy **59** Nastco/Getty Images **63** Burazin/Getty Images **64** Travis Rathbone/Trunk Archive **PART THREE 66–67** Nuria Madrid for TIME **68** Paola Kudacki for TIME **71** Courtesy of Sheryl Sandberg **72** Paola Kudacki for TIME **75** Courtesy of Sheryl Sandberg (6) **77** JPM/Getty Images **79** Varjanta/Getty Images (4) **81** (from left, from top) nito100/Getty Images, oneinchpunch/Getty Images, Sara Stadtmiller, Jen Prandato (3), Chelsea Kardokus, Jen Prandato, Kostya Kennedy, mrdoomits/Getty Images, Kyle Brett **83** Nuria Madrid for TIME **85** mrPliskin/ Getty Images **86** Ascent PKS Media/Getty Images **87** Nuria Madrid for TIME **88–89** Ajay Verma/Reuters **90** Bill Ingalls/ NASA **91** Louie Favorite/ The Journal & Constitution/ AP **92–93** Vanessa Carvalho/ Brazil Photo Press/Latin Content/Getty Images **94** Rob Tringali/Getty Images **LAST WORD 96** Benoit Decout/ REA/Redux

 For more one-of-a-kind TIME special editions and keepsakes, go to *timespecialeditions.com*.

EMOTIONAL ROBOT

Meet Pepper, the four-foot-tall robot programmed to feel emotions. Created by the Japanese company SoftBank Robotics, Pepper speaks, moves, and recognizes feelings. About 10,000 Peppers are on the job, working in nursing homes, assisting customers in Pizza Huts in Asia and standing in for Buddhist priests at Japanese funerals. Pepper not only reads emotions but also responds to them. Because they are patient and adaptable, robots like Pepper hold great promise for helping people with autism and dementia.